The
Methuselah
Formula

The Methuselah Formula

Johannes von Buttlar

BLAKE

Published by Blake Publishing Ltd,
3 Bramber Court, 2 Bramber Road, London W14 9PB, England

Published in Great Britain in 1995

First published in 1994 by bettendorf'sche
verlagsantalt GmbH in Germany

ISBN 1 85782 142 4

British Library Cataloguing-in-Publication Data:
A catalogue record for this book is available
from the British Library.

Typeset by Pearl Graphics, Hemel Hempstead

Printed in Finland by WSOY

1 3 5 7 9 10 8 6 4 2

Dedication

I dedicate this book to all holistic-thinking
pathfinders in every field of science — with the hope
of better times to come.

Acknowledgements

First and foremost I want to thank my wife and partner Elise for being an invaluable help in all my enterprises. Thanks, too, to Dr. Helmut Neuberger for editing the German version. Also, Wulfing von Rohr, who acquired interesting specialist articles for me from the United States; Heike Schäfer, who managed to complete drawing up the manuscript on computer despite little Anna; and finally my fellow aviators and my flying instructor, Captain Michael Schäfer, who read the galley proofs in his spare time.

I would also like to express my appreciation to the team at Blake Publishing, who made *The Methuselah Formula*, with so much care and love, available in the English language. In addition, Sarah Lewis-Schätz who translated the book and Jim Rickards who re-edited it for the English edition.

Johannes von Buttlar,
Sante Fe, August 1995

Contents

The Dream

CHAPTER ONE

The Game
of Life

The human race is standing at the threshold of the greatest revolution in its history. In huge strides, we are nearing the fulfilment of our oldest dream: the victory over transience, the defeat of aging and death. We have now reached the point where we possess the means to reinvent ourselves, to manufacture a new human species capable of defying Time.

The industrial age is over. Enormous and drastic scientific changes, led by biochemistry, and in particular gene technology, are offering the human race possibilities unthinkable only a few years ago. The means currently at our disposal of understanding the aging process and how it can be controlled will totally change our lives, our civilisation and our system of values.

3

The Dream

Up to now human society has been determined by the alternation of generations, by the unceasing sequence of birth, aging and death. In the natural world, as Darwin realised, death accelerates evolution – only the strongest, the most adaptable survive. And so it was in the past that the healthiest, the quickest, the most intelligent, generated progress. But qualifying all our achievements were the prospects of old age and, ultimately, death. We could change the world so long as we lived. But once we were gone, so too was our influence. This accepted and unavoidable basic truth of our existence has for millennia shaped our view of the world and the life we lived in it.

Many are of the opinion that our limited life span of eighty, ninety or one hundred years at the most is absolutely, totally and finally willed by God. And they seek consolation in the truism that, after all, every age has its advantages. However, many gerontologists – researchers of aging – hold to an equally strong faith. Namely, the certainty that the limitation of life is not the result of an inevitable evolutionary, or religious, dictate and, in principal, can therefore be extended by any number of years, depending on the knowledge we acquire and, subsequently, to what ends we use that knowledge. If human life, especially the vital active years, can be prolonged by certain methods or measures, it would mean that for the first time the human race controls time – the most valuable, irreplaceable element in our lives.

Sometimes the body is compared with a machine. It needs fuel, it needs repairs, it needs rest. Imagine you've just bought a new car. It's top of the range – smooth suspension, gleaming body work, and an engine that purrs. It's your baby and you'll take good care of it. You'll feed it with high grade petrol, lubricate its joints with the best oil money can buy, you'll send it for a regular MOT to the best garage every year and religiously, without fail, you'll wash it every Sunday morning, and wax it once a month. You're the perfect owner, you do everything right. Your car will last a long time.

But it won't last forever. Within ten years, maybe fifteen the rust will set in, the engine will pack in, and you will give in trying to keep it going. Your baby has grown old, had a good life, but is now destined for that over-populated scrap-heap in the sky.

Now go back five years again. Your beloved car hasn't collapsed into a pile of rust. It's had its fair share of wear and tear but it still goes pretty well. Supposing a scientist with an amazing discovery, a company with huge piles of cash and a publicist with the most persuasive marketing plan the consumer has ever consumed enter the scene. A new oil is born. In effect, it's a drug. You put it into the engine and it guarantees no friction whatsoever. Your engine parts will now last just about forever. Another scientist joins the team and with the profits from the first product invents a new spray that makes rust disappear and guarantees it will never reappear. With these two products you can keep your car from aging further, the bodywork intact and the engine running. Other parts like the gear box may go, but they're replaceable. It's not mint but it'll keep chugging as long as you do.

Of course you could always trade it in and fork out for a spanking new version that will stay new for ever and ever and ever . . .

If a scientist discovers this, if the companies put the money in, *if* this, *if* that . . . *If the same were true for the human body, what then?*

The Dream

That essential word 'if', is about to be replaced by 'when'. For it is no longer a matter for conjecture that scientists around the world are actively seeking, *and finding*, ways of bypassing the signs of aging. Gene research has recently led to many startling discoveries concerning DNA – the basic coding of all life on earth. Scientists now believe that there is a self-destruct button, some might say an evolutionary safety mechanism, programmed into our cells that ensures our death. They have also *proved* it can be outwitted. Nutritionists are proclaiming to the world the wonders of various vitamins and enzymes which can prevent and, in some cases reverse, major killers such as cancer and heart disease that claim millions of lives every year. Investigations into our immune system have shown that it's possible to strengthen many times over the barriers against disease and infectious illnesses. There has also been an upsurge of interest in areas outside of 'conventional' medicine such as shamanism, yoga and meditation, many of whose practitioners are renowned for their ability to regenerate their bodies and stay youthful through relaxation and positive mental thinking.

In total this amounts to about two hundred research projects concentrating on achieving a drastic prolongation of the active, vital years of our lives. Proponents of gerontology are following the vision of a human life expectancy which can be measured in centuries, not decades. They are pursuing a utopia, which was once dreamed by Gilgamesh, the king of the Sumerians 6000 years ago. They are hoping to make real the 'fountain of eternal youth', a mystical source which was searched for in the alchemist's kitchens and by wanderers in the New World. As with all these endeavours, it is a question of finding the ways and means of dying as late as possible and staying as youthful as possible – a quest that I call the Methuselah Formula.

Numerous experiments have already successfully extended the life span of animals. We will be next. If you doubt this, consider the investment being made. In the USA, the Genoma project, which aims to completely decipher the human hereditary program, has received funding of three *billion* dollars. Many scientists believe this will prove to be the decisive trump card in the game against death. For if complete knowledge of the gene card of man is attainable, nearly all illnesses will eventually be eliminated, and genetic manipulation will offer a way of outwitting what was once an inevitable path to old age.

And that's just the tip of the iceberg. Experts in all disciplines are chipping away at our tombstones. A new discovery is made almost every day. A fusing of different approaches is leading to a greater understanding of how the human body works. From the tiniest molecule in DNA to the nebulous powers of the mind, a map is being drawn. Somewhere on that map is the fountain of youth. And someday soon we will find it. It will happen in my lifetime, and it will happen in yours.

Taken together these investigations cannot be ignored as just another departure down wish fulfilment lane. They represent the greatest scientific leap for humankind since the advent of quantum mechanics.

We can be ostriches if we want, stick our heads deep in the sand and pretend it isn't happening. It won't stop it. Or we can look at the subject more closely, understand why it *is* happening and consider what the consequences for ourselves and our children might be. This book is a starting point, an overview of current developments and thinking and considers briefly what the future may hold for us and how we can shape it by actively changing our dietary and living habits.

But to fully understand anything, we must first unearth the root causes. The quest for immortality is as old as humanity itself. History and myth is riddled with stories of the search for eternal youth. From the first cave dweller who looked at the stars and wondered at their place in the great scheme of things, through to the great Greek and Roman thinkers, the hopeful adventurers of the New World and ultimately to the gene-splicers at their keyboards in laboratories in every continent, the urge to comprehend and solve the greatest mystery of them all has been, and still is, all-consuming.

As you will see the search was one of high hopes fed by myth and hearsay but they nearly always ended in disappointment. Today, however, there is no dead end. Today, the story is very different and each of us has a part to play in its concluding chapter.

Methuselah, in all his wisdom, would have been proud . . .

CHAPTER TWO

In the Age
of the Gods

The young king was accompanied only by his personal bodyguard on his way to the mysterious oasis in the Libyan desert. He had left behind a huge army camped at the Nile Delta. And for this final part of the journey he had also declined the services of his elite battalion — fifty impressive warriors in shining breastplates, with magnificent bronze helmets and round shields, on which was emblazoned the eagle of Zeus, the heraldic emblem of the Macedonians.

The king was ambitious. With his men hungry for victory, he had set out to crush the mighty Persian empire. And succeeded. Soon, he would conquer the world. He knew it in his heart. But at this particular moment, he had a more pressing engagement. He was about to meet one of the most famous seers of his time, the oracle of the god Zeus-Amon in the oasis of Siwa. Alexander, whom posterity was to name 'the Great', wanted to learn the truth here about himself, his life and his fate. Doubt drove him through the desert, until, after a three-day, ride the palm trees and the temple in the oasis appeared before him. The local oracle in Delphi had foretold him fame as a world conqueror, but qualified his predictions of glory with a warning that he should expect a very short life. Alexander had never been able to accept this warning. If, as many had said, he was actually a son of Zeus, then by rights he should be immortal. If he was immortal, how could he be prophesied such a fleeting life? The only one who knew with certainty was his godly father to whom he could not speak directly. But his father's representative here in the middle of the desert, might provide some answers . . . if the gods wished it.

Up to now prophecies and oracles had played a central part throughout Alexander's life. Born as the son of the Macedonian king Philip and queen Olympia in 357 BC, seers and interpreters of signs had, when he was still very young, foreseen a great future for him. His teacher, the universally learned Aristotle, aroused his cultural interest and his thirst for knowledge. His models were the great heroes of Greek literature, especially Achilles, the legendary hero of Homer's *Iliad*.

At the age of sixteen, he had become acting king, while his father was away leading a military campaign against the Byzantines. One year later he assumed command of the army. After the murder of Philip in 336 BC, he held the throne proper and wasted no time in extending Macedonia's borders thus consolidating his supremacy in Greece. In the spring of 334 BC, he started the war against the Persians and with 36,000 soldiers crossed the Hellespont (Dardanelles), which separate Europe and Asia. Systematically, he pushed back the great Persian power, which had previously controlled Asia Minor unchallenged, until in November 333 BC it finally came to the final battle near Issus, which is today known to all. Even though the Persian leader managed to flee in time, Alexander's bold cavalry attack on the chariot of king Darius was decisive. Alexander carried on triumphantly to Persian-occupied Phoenicia where Darius sent him two offers of peace. Finally, in desperation, he even offered Alexander half of the Persian empire – all the provinces up to the Euphrates in present day Iraq. Alexander declined. He had other aims to pursue.

Although strategically unimportant, he made first for Egypt. In his youth he had listened, fascinated, to the stories which Aristotle had told him of this wondrous desert country. Egypt was the land of secrets, in which priests of wisdom had been researching the secrets of life and death for thousands of years. Alexander was convinced that the realization of the Delphian oracle about his early death could only be prevented, if at all, by the wise men of Egypt.

When Alexander the Great reached the oasis of Siwa on that day in November in the year 332 BC, his coming had already been announced by messengers, and so it was that he was met by a procession of priests for a ceremonial welcome, led by the high priest of Zeus-Amon. The venerable old man's body was emaciated by age and the extreme desert climate. His head was shaven, his face punctuated by clear, piercing eyes. He was dressed in white robes with leopard skin draped

11

over the shoulders, as was tradition. In his hands he held aloft a powerful sceptre of cedarwood, crowned with the symbol of Zeus-Amon: a ram's head. Alexander dismounted from his horse reverently, fell to his knees and bowed deeply and humbly before the priest.

'Greetings! Rise, Greek, son of Zeus-Amon. I am your servant, lover of the gods,' the old high priest said with a trembling voice. Tears of emotion welled in his eyes in response to the young king's gesture. This man, who had freed Egypt from Persian rule, was humble enough to lay himself prostrate in recognition of the high priest's stature.

'I have come here to find answers', Alexander answered, surprised by the priest's reactions. 'If I am, as you say, the son of Amon, how do I then achieve the immortality which is my birth right?'

'Go to Karnak, to the temple of your father, the great god Amon,' the oracle priest advised him.

A week later the Macedonian army arrived at the ancient Egyptian capital of Thebes. Here, Alexander sought out the temple district of Karnak, the 'city of God', the God Amon or Amun. He was again glitteringly received as a son of god.

In the cool of the holy temple a high priest told him the story of Cambyses, son of the Persian king Cyrus, who had come there before Alexander, also chasing immortality. The Egyptians hated Cambyses, for instead of offering himself humbly, he had led a bloody campaign against their country. And when he had received an unsatisfactory answer to his questions, he destroyed the temple of Amun in Karnak so thoroughly that right up to Alexander's day many of the powerful obelisks lay on the floor and the ritual districts remained completely destroyed. The bloodthirsty leader then moved southwards to the country of the 'long-living Ethiopians'. His scouts were sent ahead under the pretext of bringing the king of Ethiopia presents and asking him whether the rumour about the longevity of his people was true. A prince led them to a fountain and asked them to wash in it. A scent like that of violets came from the water, and their skin became shiny and smooth, as if they had bathed in oil. The scouts returned excited, describing the water as 'So weak nothing swam on it, neither wood nor a lighter material. Everything sank to the bottom'.

As fascinated as Cambyses was by their report, he never reached his destination; the Ethiopian resistance to the Persian army was too vehement and his soldiers were too weakened by malaria and the blazing sun of the Sudan.

'But you are loved by the gods, Alexander,' declared the temple priest as he finished his story, 'and luck shines in your favour. At this moment Candace, the queen of the Ethiopians, is in Thebes. Go and speak to her. Perhaps she will disclose to you the secret of longevity.'

What followed was a classic love story, to be compared to the couplings of Solomon and the Queen of Sheba or Caesar and Cleopatra. Alexander fell in love with the beautiful African, and she promised to 'lead him into the cave, where the gods assembled'. Again accompanied only by his bodyguard, he followed her to the capital Shamar and after spending some time together in her palace she led him to the holy place as a farewell.

One of Alexander's chroniclers described the scene. 'He entered with several soldiers and saw a light haze and the vault glimmered as if lit up by stars. The outer manifestation of the gods appeared in physical form as a crowd served them silently. At first Alexander was shocked and surprised, but he remained to see what would happen, for he glimpsed resting beings whose eyes shone like rays of light . . . And then one of them spoke "Greetings, Alexander. Do you know who I am?" And he answered: "No, master." The other one said: "I am Sesonkhusis, the king who conquered the world and who has risen up to the gods." '

He was then invited to go to the god Serapis, to the 'creator and supervisor of the whole universe'. Alexander asked him the ultimate question that had plagued him all his life: 'How many years have I still to live?'

The god remained silent. Dejected, Alexander turned to Sesonkhusis for solace and the god king said: 'Although I have risen up to the gods, I have not been granted as much luck as you. I have indeed conquered the whole world and many peoples, but nobody remembers my name. After your death your memory will live on and you will therefore not die. Your fame will grant you immortality.'

The Macedonian rode back to Thebes in the depths of despair. He searched within himself for comfort and eventually he found it. He would accept the god's wise words. He would achieve immortality through great deeds. He therefore considered his initial ambition, to conquer the world, his true calling in life. And in doing so he would never give up hope, for on the way who knew what he might find.

In Thebes he heard of the Indian gymnosophists, 'the naked wise men', who had apparently overcome death. Rumours told of them living totally naked in the snowy mountains of the Himalayas, suffering not from cold, hunger, or thirst. It was said they directed their spirit towards eternity. They had lived to one thousand years and could remember events which took place so long ago that their contemporaries could only remember them from myths and legends.

Alexander determined to conquer India, and on the way seek eternal life. But although his army had defeated the entire Persian empire and advanced as far as Bactria, it was beaten back to a tributary of the Indus, the border river to India. After a series of costly battles, the Macedonian finally gave up hope of his dream and began a retreat back to Alexandria in Egypt, which he had selected to become the capital of his empire.

But on the long, arduous march through the Persian highlands Alexander fell ill. When he finally reached Babylon he was severely weakened. Lying on his death bed he summoned the priest of the god Marduk to him. 'Tell me, priest,' he said, 'how have I, the son of Zeus-Amon, incurred the wrath of the gods?' Like many before him, the high priest of Marduk didn't answer directly, but rather told Alexander a version of *The Epic of Gilgamesh*, the oldest handed-down legend known to humanity.

Over twenty-six centuries before Alexander, Gilgamesh, King of Uruk, had devoted his life to the same quest. Two-thirds god, one-third human, he was one of the first mortals to seek immortality. The earliest written version was produced in 2000 BC in Babylon. A complete copy inscribed on twelve tablets was found by British archaeologists in the middle of the 19th century, in the ruins of the library of the learned Assyrian king Ashurbanipal in Nineveh near Mosul in present day northern Iraq. First published in 1876 as the 'Chaldean portrayal of the Flood', the legend of Gilgamesh was still being spread in the 19th century by roaming story-tellers in the Caucasus area.

And so it was that Gurdjieff, the great Caucasian initiate, wrote in his autobiography *Meetings with Remarkable People*, that his father had told him a story which, since long-forgotten times, had been passed down from generation to generation, and which turned out to be a reproduction of the Gilgamesh Epic. The greatest literary heritage of Mesopotamia thereby remained alive for four thousand years.

Portrayals of the 'lion conqueror' Gilgamesh on the seals of the Hurrians and the Hittites also testify to the spreading of the legend in the whole of the Near East. In the introduction to the epic, it says of Gilgamesh:

'He has seen secret things,
what is hidden to man, he knows.
He has brought news
from the times of the Flood.
He also undertook journeys to far-off shores
arduously and in difficulty.
He returned and wrote down all his trials and
tribulations on a stony pillar.'

His forefather, the first king of Uruk, was regarded as the product of a union between the sun god Shamash and a human woman, but Gilgamesh himself was regarded as the son of the goddess Ninsun, so that he claimed the right to bestow on himself the epithet 'divine'.

He was a good, wise and fair king, who enlarged the temple area of Uruk and had the city fortified with strong walls. The epic called him 'the good shepherd of Uruk'. But the more intensively he dedicated his life to the service of the gods and the people, the more he felt himself to be a homeless person, a hermaphrodite, who looked for his place in the world of the people and of the gods. He became increasingly aware of his own origins and he was troubled by the question of whether he himself was now a god – and thereby immortal – or a mere human. And so he poured out his distress to his ancestor Shamash:

> 'In my city man dies:
> my heart is despondent.
> Man passes away:
> my heart is heavy . . .
> The tallest person cannot
> stretch up to the heavens,
> the widest person
> cannot cover the earth.
> Am I also condemned to this?'

'When the gods created man, they assigned him death as well,' the god replied, without answering Gilgamesh's question, 'and they reserved eternal life for themselves.'

The gods sent Enkidu (Enki's creation) to distract Gilgamesh from his troublesome musings. This being was half-man, half-animal, strong, naked, unkempt, with hair all over his body. They clashed with each other. Enkidu firstly challenged Gilgamesh to a fight, only to then become his friend. Before that Enkidu encountered a temple prostitute. He made love to her for six days and seven nights, 'until he was satiated from her charms' – and in doing so was transformed into a man. He went to the animals, with which he had lived before, but they fled from him. The child of nature had lost his innocence; the process of civilisation had begun.

After they had become friends, Gilgamesh revealed to Enkidu his fear of death. His companion knew what to do. He must go to the 'apartment of the gods' in the 'cedar mountains', for, if Shamash stood by him, the immortals there could make him one of them. The 'home of the gods' was protected by the ogre Humbaba, who was strong but simple and could be outwitted.

The heroes set off immediately, killed Humbaba, and would have reached their destination, if the goddess Ishtar had not 'descended' near their camp. She saw Gilgamesh as he was bathing to wash the wounds suffered during the battle with the ogre, and 'cast an eye on his beauty'. 'Come, Gilgamesh, be my lover,' she invited the king, but he had other things on his mind and ignored her entreaties. Offended, the rejected goddess plotted revenge and asked her father Anu, to send the 'divine bull', to have Gilgamesh crushed but the heroes managed to overcome this monster too.

Anu was enraged. 'As the bull of heaven and Humbaba have been killed, they will both have to die,' he declared. But as Gilgamesh was a relation, the death sentence, in reality, only affected Enkidu. Gilgamesh's friend fell ill and passed away after twelve days. Gilgamesh kneeled at his corpse for six days and seven nights and would not allow him to be buried, 'until a worm fell out of his nose' and he realised that his companion's fate was sealed.

'Gilgamesh cried bitterly for his friend, he shouted his pain out to the far-off lands. "Must I also die? Am I not like Enkidu? My inner being is filled with wrath, and so I am shouting to the far-off lands."'

But then he had an idea. He had to go to Utnapish-tim, 'who was loved by the gods'. The only person who had overcome death, Utnapishtim was the Sumerian Noah who, together with his wife, had survived the Flood because the god Enki warned him in time and instructed him to build an ark. He alone was therefore granted the privilege of living in Tilmun, the 'land of eternal life', and it was to him that Gilgamesh wanted to go, in order that he learn secret of immortality.

The way to Tilmun lay westwards, a long and arduous treck through a vast expanse of desert, where Gilgamesh fought with lions, and over the Mashu mountain range, which was guarded by 'scorpion people'. Here he roamed through gloomy ravines and dark tunnels, until he finally reached the sea shore at the other side.

A brief search led him to a 'garden of precious stones'. Then he discovered a tavern, which he entered. It belonged to the taverner Siduri, who was frightened of the unkempt king until he poured out his sorrows and asked her the way to Utnapishtim. Siduri answered:

'Oh, Gilgamesh, where do you want to run to?
you will not find the life that you are searching for!
for as the gods once created man,
they assigned death to mankind,
they took life for themselves!
So fill your stomach, oh Gilgamesh,
amuse yourself by day and by night,
prepare yourself a festival of joy every day
with dancing and playing by day and by night!
Let your children be radiantly clean,

wash your head and bathe in water,
look to the child, who is taking your hand,
let a woman enjoy your favours at your breast
– for such is everything that a man desires!'

Gilgamesh was not impressed by her speech, and insisted Siduri give him a straight answer. Finally, she gave in saying: 'There was never a ferry of any type and no-one has crossed the sea since the beginning of time. The crossing is difficult, the way is perilous, for deadly waters lie inbetween. The continuation of your journey is impossible. But if you insist on trying, Utnapishtim has a boatman called Ur-shanabi. He fells young pines in the woods. Go and show yourself to him!'

Gilgamesh found Ur-shanabi and persuaded the old boatman to take him across the deadly sea. Ur-shanabi set about felling three hundred pines and made from them tall poles that would help them reach their destination in safety.

On the other side of the sea, 'at the mouth of the rivers', Utnapishtim saw the boat coming and welcomed Ur-shanabi and the sinister stranger:

'Why are your cheeks hollow,
your face haggard,
your heart closed,
your appearance drained,
and wrath inside you?
Your face is that of someone who has travelled far,
tanned by cold and heat,
dressed only in a lion skin
you roam through the land?'

Gilgamesh answered by telling Utnapishtim his story:

'How could I be silent?
my friend, who I loved, turned to dust.
Am I not like him?
Must I not one day lie down
to never get up again?'

'But why must you abandon yourself to wrath?'
Utnapishtim persisted. 'As the gods created you from
the flesh of the gods and of man, as the gods have
created you as they did your father and mother, death
is one day unavoidable, the same for Gilgamesh as for
a fool . . .

No-one sees death
no-one sees its face
no-one hears its voice.
Cruel death simply mows people down.
Sometimes we build a house,
sometimes just a nest,
and then brothers, who inherit it, divide it.
Sometimes enmity reigns in the land,
and then the rivers rise and cause floods.
Dragonflies drift on the river,
their faces look into the face of the sun,
and then suddenly there is nothing left there.
Sleep and death are so similar,
and nevertheless it is impossible
to draw the picture of death.'

Utnapishtim further told Gilgamesh, how he himself
attained immortality (the story of the Flood) and advised
him to try to stay awake, as he had once stayed awake,
for six days and seven nights. (According to Sumerian
tradition this is how long the Flood lasted.) But

Gilgamesh failed the test. As soon as he sat down, 'he was overcome by sleep like a haze', and he didn't wake up until seven nights later.

Resigned, he decided to give up the search for immortality. But as he said goodbye to Utnapishtim, the latter offered him a present. He revealed where Gilgamesh could find 'a well protected secret of the gods': a rejuvenating plant. Gilgamesh fetched it from the bottom of the sea, crossed the sea once again and set off on his way home to Uruk. But as he climbed into a fountain in the desert to bathe, a serpent smelt the aroma of the plant, fetched it out of his pocket and carried it away. Totally despondent, Gilgamesh returned to his camp, sat down and wept. He knew now that he was destined to fail in his life's quest.

When, however, he finally returned to Uruk and saw the mighty walls he had ordered to be built, he began to understand the real meaning of immortality: to survive in the human memory through works and deeds.

In the twelfth tablet the gods at least reward Gilgamesh's insight and let Enkidu return from the underworld. This is the first and oldest instance of a resurrection myth and thus a forerunner of Christianity.

From the evidence we have today, we know that Gilgamesh was not simply a fictional creation. He did actually live, though quite how much of the epic is truth and how much is hearsay is a matter for debate. These, however, are the facts. His name appears in the royal lists of the first dynasty of Uruk. He lived from 2600 BC, and we can gather from an inscription of one of his successors, Anam of Urak, that the latter further extended 'the mighty walls, which Gilgamesh erected'. The gods blessed him, if not with immortality, at the very least with a very long life. According to the royal list he died at the age of 126.

If we are to believe the Sumerian royal lists, such longevity was not exceptional. Gilgamesh's forefather Meskiaggascheir, son of the Shamash, reached the age of 325; his successor Enmekar, 420; his grandfather Lugalbanda, 'the shepherd', made it all the way to 1200 years. These fantastic lives are only exceeded by the kings of 'the first dynasty of Kish', who ruled directly after the Flood. Etana, was their oldest king at the age of 1500 years while the youngest, Mesza, reached 140 years. It is only after Gilgamesh that the monarchs of this era started dying at ages which, by our standards, are more credible. Their reigns ranged between six and thirty-eight years. On the other hand, the lives of the kings before the Flood are, according to legend, excessively longer.

An examination of the Sumerian royal lists reveals the following staggering lifespans:

Alulim, king of Nunki	28 800 years
Alalgar, king of Nunki	36 000 years
Enmeenluanna, king of Bad-Tibira	43 200 years
Enmeengalanna, king of Bad-Tibira	28 800 years
Dumuzi, king of Bad-Tibira	36 000 years
Ensibzianna, king of Larak	28 800 years
Enmeenduranna, king of Sippar	21 000 years
En-du-du, king of Shuruppak	18 600 years

Of course, age was probably exaggerated to imply stature and encourage reverence in the commoners for their rulers. Even so, ages referred to in many myths seem high and the possibility that they at least reflect a generally longer life expectancy than we enjoy today should not be dismissed out of hand. A closer look at

---

the ages of prominent figures in the Bible adds weight to this theory. In Genesis chapter 5, the following ages are given for Adam and his descendants:

Adam	930 years
Seth	912 years
Enos	905 years
Cainan	910 years
Mahalaleel	895 years
Jared	962 years
Enoch	365 years
('and he was not, for God took him')	
Methuselah	969 years
Lamech	777 years
Noah	950 years

However, after the Flood, which took place in Noah's six hundredth year, life expectation reduced considerably, as the 11th chapter of Genesis shows:

Shem	930 years
Arphaxad	438 years
Salah	433 years
Eber	464 years
Peleg	239 years
Reu	239 years
Serug	230 years
Nahor	148 years
Terah	205 years
Abram	175 years
Isaac	180 years
Jacob	147 years
Joseph	110 years

Not until Moses did the lifespan of humans find its way to a believable one hundred and twenty years. The ages given in the Bible appear fantastic, but as with the Sumerian kings, they cannot be explained simply by attributing to them exaggeration or arbitrary filling of possible gaps in information handed down over the years. For, as can clearly be seen from the list shown above, the life expectancy of biblical figures decreases in a gradual curve.

In his book *The Search for Eden*, biochemist Siegfried Scherer cites these figures as evidence of 'a biological process, as yet unknown,' being responsible. In a contribution for the Jerusalem bible lexicon, he expanded on his theory and speculated on the possible causes:

'The living conditions probably clearly changed after the flood. Biblical evidence for this is: the decreasing age, the appointment of the rainbow as the national sign and permission to eat meat after the flood. The . . . steam belt (of the earth) could have produced an even climate before the flood. Irrigation did not result . . . from rain, but from another kind of water circulation... water springing from the ground moistened the earth. There can be no rainbow without rain.'

According to Scherer, the dense cloud covering the earth at that time could have protected the inhabitants of earth from radiation more effectively than today's atmosphere.

Maybe, like those attributed to the Sumerians, the ages given in the Bible were merely symbolic. Immortality was considered a privilege of the gods; if a man lived long, it indicated closeness to some higher power. It follows that an era in which people generally lived longer, was therefore to be revered as a golden age of harmony with creation, whereas a short life implied estrangement with the divine laws of the cosmos.

The life span of the biblical patriarchs portrays a historical framework after the Flood and it, at the very least, qualifies such an allegorical interpretation. In my book *Adam's Planet* I proved, using Sumerian and Arcadian texts, that Abraham was a historical figure and not, as some may believe, the product of handed-down legend. He can be placed, with some certainty, in the last days of the Sumerian city state – around 2000 BC. In the chronicle of the Sumerian king Amar-Sin, he appears as Ibrum, fathering his son Isaac in his hundredth year. The chronicle asks 'Who would have said unto Abraham, that Sarah should have given children suck?' And in the Bible: 'For I have born him a son in his old age.' (Gen. 21.7).

It is likely that these tales of excessive old age in biblical texts and oral legends were the initial impetus that inspired Alexander the Great to explore the world, as once Gilgamesh did, in search of the secret of eternal life. Across the ancient world rumours circulated of a secret place, in which either the taking of a herb or a plant, or bathing in a fountain or lake could bestow upon the recipient eternal life.

The celts told of the goddess Idun who, on the island of Avalon, watched over apples for the gods, the consumption of which brought rejuvenation. The apple appears as the symbol of fertility and life in many legends of the ancient world. Greek mythology refers to the 'golden apples of the Hesperides' which were watched over by the 'daughters of the West' in a garden on the 'island of the blessed' in the western sea. Heracles received instructions through the Delphian oracle to get three of the golden apples from the garden of the Hesperides. 'When that is done,' so the promise went, 'you will become one of the immortals.'

Other heroes were subjects of cautionary tales against the arrogance of trying to acquire immortality. The privilege of the gods was not to be sought lightly, and those who tried often had to atone for their actions. Tantalus stole nectar and ambrosia, youth-giving elixirs, from the table of the gods. He suffered a severe and sadistic retribution. In the underworld he was made to stand chest high in water. Above him grew the most exquisite, mouth-watering fruits, six inches out of reach. He was to remain there for all eternity, tormented by insatiable hunger and a relentless thirst. A fitting and typical punishment. Odysseus, however, showed better judgement by declining the immortality promised him by the nymph Calypso, for in return he would have had to remain with her forever.

The Greek poet Hesiod concentrated on similar themes in a work about the Arcadian past in which the members of the 'golden race' reached an age of at least one hundred years, all the while staying fresh and young. When their time eventually came, they lay themselves down to die in peace and quiet, 'as if they were lying in Morpheus arms'. According to Hesiod there then followed the 'silver race', also granted a childhood of one hundred years. But they didn't show the same humility or reverence before the gods, and were consequently banished to the underworld by Zeus, where their extreme longevity proved to be a particularly hard punishment.

The Greeks believed that in the far north – in the land of Hyperboreas – and on the mythical 'islands of the blessed' somewhere out in the Atlantic, perfect people existed who lived for a thousand years. Pindar described them thus: 'Their hair was crowned with golden bayleaves; they celebrated merry feasts and knew nothing of illness or decline.'

The Arabs were also able to offer an elusive fountain of youth to lubricate the hopes of the common man. They called it the 'source of the water of life'. According to tradition this source was supposedly only discovered by chance. When the legendary conqueror of the Moors, El Cid, washed a dry fish in the waters, it suddenly came to life before his very eyes. With great presence of mind El Cid immediately jumped after it, and behold, of course he became immortal.

He was one of the few lucky ones. In most tales, the concoctions and remedies for eternal youth and the people or gods who benefit from them are always inaccessible. Those who seek them must undertake long and terrible journeys. Many of those who set out return empty handed and old. Their grail appears tantalisingly close, only to disappear as the heroes strive desperately to complete an endless wild goose chase. This theme of ever-shifting sources can be found in references to the Hindu fountain of youth and the Hebrew river of immortality, which rises in Eden. But the prize for the most impossible place to reach goes to a Greek source of youth, which lay in the jungles of Jupiter. There the nymph Juventas was said to be transformed – into a clear, sweet river, whose waters revived youth and health in those who were lucky enough to swim in them.

The similarities between these many legends are not accidental. Over the years the great themes were circulated by word of mouth or rewritten and augmented.

Elaboration was commonplace and thus the story of real figures like Alexander the Great, who died after hearing the *Epic of Gilgamesh*, became the stuff of legend. It didn't take long for Alexander's achievements to be glorified. Up until the Middle Ages the *Legend of Alexander*, which was wrongly attributed to the Greek historian Callisthenes from Olynthus, enjoyed great popularity. In the Islamic world and as far as Ethiopia the work was widely circulated, just as the *Epic of Gilgamesh* had been two thousand years before. Several of the motifs in the *Legend of Alexander* refer directly to the Gilgamesh epic. In this version of the story, Alexander leaves Egypt to stray in the desert and discover the 'secrets of the sky, the stars and the planets'. He makes his way into the land of darkness and at the edge of the desert reaches a mountain called Mushas. After a long search he discovers a 'straight path' and instructs his guard to wait for him at the end of it. He travels on alone for a further twelve days and twelve nights, until he perceives the 'radiating gleam of an angel' and realises he's reached the top of the mountain, 'on which the whole world rests'.

'Who are you and for what reason are you here, mortal?' the angel asks. 'How did you penetrate this darkness, as no other person has managed?'

'God himself led me here and gave me the strength to reach this place, which is Paradise,' the Macedonian answers.

After a long conversation about God and the people Alexander is refused entry to Paradise, but is instead offered a consolation. 'I want to tell you how you can live without dying,' the angel says. 'In Arabia, God has inflicted the blackness of impenetrable darkness.

Therein is hidden a treasure of knowledge, a fountain that flows with the water of life. Whoever drinks from it, if only a tiny drop, will never die.'

'In which part of the earth is this fountain?' Alexander asks eagerly.

The angel's cryptic answer: 'Ask those who are the heirs of this knowledge.'

From that day, according to the *Legend of Alexander*, the king asked every priest and wise man that he met: 'Have you ever read in your books that God created a place of darkness, where knowledge is hidden and where the fountain is situated, which is called the fountain of life?'

Although the *Legend of Alexander* does not explain exactly where this secret place is to be found, a series of middle age exegetes (interpreters) believed they had found the answer. Many scholarly theories were offered – he wandered to the 'end of the earth': to India, to the mouth of the Ganges, to the biblical river of paradise, Pison, or on one of the offshore islands to the gates to Paradise. The 'Alexander novel' written in the 12th century by Lambert le Tort and Alexandre de Paris went as far as to name three fountains: one which bestows immortality, the second which rejuvenates and the third which brings the dead back to life. In addition, the 'Alexander novel' describes the discovery of the fountain of youth by a sixty-five year old companion of Alexander, who, by drinking a drop from it, 'once again gained the skin of a thirty year old'.

These stories spurred countless quests in the Europe of the middle ages. The lure of immortality surpassed trifles such as the beautiful and endless treasures which could be found in the depths of India, of which there were always rumours. Adventurers and discoverers, often with Royal sanction, engaged in a flurry of expeditions to find the end of the world. But between Europe and India lay the kingdom of the Saracens, the infidels, the enemies of Christianity – a bastion, which for centuries blocked access to the Indus and the Ganges. Then, in 1499, the breakthrough was achieved. For the first time Europeans, the fleet of the Portuguese Vasco da Gama, sailed around the Cape of Good Hope at the southern tip of Africa and reached India by sea. Seven years before, travelling in the opposite direction, three Spanish ships under the command of the Genoan Christopher Columbus had landed on a group of islands, which were off the shore of an unknown continent. Columbus was convinced that the earth was a sphere and that one had to reach India sometime, if one only sailed far enough westwards. He named the group of islands he discovered as the 'West Indies' and called their inhabitants 'Indios'. Were these islands off the shore of Paradise, and was the legendary Fountain of Youth hidden on one of them?

When Ponce de León, the adventurer who had been promoted to the rank of governor of the islands of Hispaniola (Haiti) and Puerto Rico, was present at the interrogation of captured American Indians in 1511, the search for the wonder fountain gained a new impetus. The natives enthused about an island in the north called Bimini, on which there were pearls and other riches, and whose waters made old men regain their vitality and virility.

Ponce de León, himself no longer so young, sat up and took notice. He had not been deaf to frequent talk in Europe of the existence of such a place: was *he* finally on its trail? He despatched news to the Spanish king Ferdinand who, many historians are now convinced, immediately gave the discovery of the fountain of youth absolute priority over all other projects in the New World. On 23 February, 1512, he sent Ponce de León a royal charter for an expedition into the area north of the island Hispaniola and advised the admiralty to support the governor and put the best ships at his disposal, in order to explore the Biminis. 'After you have reached the islands and have discovered what they contain, you will report back to me,' he commanded de León.

In March 1513, the Spanish fleet put to sea and set sail for the north. But instead of finding one island, they came across dozens; they landed on each and sampled – with less than dramatic results – the water of innumerable sources. On Easter Sunday, 'Pascua de Flores' in Spanish, they finally sighted a long coast line: a new land, which de León named 'Florida'. The Spanish wasted no time in landing, crossed the jungles and swamps of the 'island', and drank water wherever they could find it. When they then encountered natives, who seemed very young for their alleged age, these were interrogated, partly under torture. Again and again they heard of legends which seemed to confirm their belief in the existence of the fountain of youth.

Some of the native tribes spoke of a god Olelbis who, when creating humans, joined heaven and earth together with a ladder. At the top he placed two springs, one for drinking and the other for bathing. If a man became old, he only had to climb to the top, drink and bathe, in order to immediately regain his youth.

Ponce de León led many unsuccessful attempts to find such treasures but it did not discourage him, or his expedition. On the contrary, a year later, in 1514, the priest Petrus Martyr wrote to Pope Leo X:

'325 miles north of Hispaniola there is supposedly an island called Boyuca alias Ananeo, which according to those who have explored its interior, has a remarkable fountain whose water rejuvenates the old. May your Holiness not think that this is said lightly and rashly, for word of it has spread through the whole court as the truth, so that everyone here, many of whom differ from the common people through wisdom and fortune, consider it true.'

So in 1521, Ponce de León once again set off for Florida, 'in search of the holy fountain, which was so praised by the natives, and the river, whose water rejuvenates the old', as the Spanish historian Antonio de Herrera y Tordesillas wrote in his *Historia General de las Indias*. He stepped up his search for the elusive river in Florida or the source on the island of Bimini. But, as with so many before him in legend and reality, the seeking of eternal life delivered Ponce de León an early death. A native's arrow pierced the heart of the Conquistador and brought the organised Spanish 'fountain of youth expedition' to an abrupt end.

During the Rococo period, an era notorious for its alchemists and quacks, interest in immortality was revived. But this time it was not to be found in a distant source; the prize lay much closer to home to those who knew where to find it, or perhaps more accurately, how to make it. A great initiate of the secret sciences — or was he a cunning charlatan? — came to the royal courts of Europe, to promise vain and aging ladies-in-waiting a tonic to restore youthful vitality. The magician presented himself as the best evidence of its indisputable effectiveness . . . He didn't seem to age.

He went by the name 'Count of Saint Germain' and his contemporaries called him 'the sphinx of the 18th century'. Great minds considered him highly and took his claims very seriously. To Voltaire, the famous Enlightenment philosopher, he was 'the man who knows everything and never dies'.

In 1758, the aged Countess de Gergy attended a ball given by Madame Pompadour in the chateau of Versailles near Paris. Saint Germain was also invited. It occurred to her that the count was very like a man she had met fifty years before in Venice. She had accompanied her husband there in his position as the king's envoy. And so she took heart and mentioned to the count that she had probably met his father in 1710. 'But no, Madame,' the count replied casually, 'it has been a long time indeed since I lost my father, but I myself lived in Venice at the end of the last and at the beginning of this century and had the honour of being introduced to you. You were then gracious enough to value my little barcaroles, which we used to sing together.'

'Forgive me, Count, but that is really not possible, for the Count of Saint Germain who I then knew was at least forty five years old and you do not seem to have reached that age even today.'

'I have always considered myself lucky in making myself favourably disposed to ladies,' Saint Germain flirted.

'At that time you called yourself Marquis Balletti,' the countess continued.

'And your memory, Countess Gergy, is as good today as it was fifty years ago.'

'That is thanks to a potion that you gave me then at our first meeting. You really are an extraordinary man. But how is it possible?'

'Madame, I am very old,' the count replied.

'Old! You must be a hundred years, at least.'

'That is very possible.'

This dialogue was recorded by Madame de Hausset, a lady-in-waiting to Madame Pompadour the widowed Countess d'Adhemar. Hers is the most exact description of the mysterious man — of medium height, with black hair and a brown complexion, lively intelligent features and elegant movements. He was a man with the best of manners, witty, inconspicuous, but tastefully dressed, an excellent piano player and master of various instruments. He was renowned as a superb painter who had developed special colours which gave his works unique brilliance. He had mastered the most important European languages — French, English, German, Italian, Spanish and Portuguese — so well, that not even natives could detect the slightest note of an accent. Scholars also confirmed his excellent knowledge of Latin and Greek, along with a more surprising affinity for Sanskrit, Chinese and Arabian languages which, it is said, he learnt 'during his longer stays in Asia'. The only thing that pointed to his riches was a handful of diamonds, which he wore in rings and on his snuffbox.

At the ball, the count told of past events in such detail and so vividly that many guests could not help thinking that he had experienced them personally.

'Did you?' Madame Pompadour asked him, according to the memoirs of her lady-in-waiting.

'I have a very good memory and have studied French history very thoroughly,' the Count replied. 'Sometimes I get enjoyment, not from pretending, but from at least making people believe, that I lived in ancient times.'

'But nevertheless you refuse to divulge your age, saying only you are "very old",' said Pompadour. 'The

Countess de Gergy, who was ambassadress in Venice fifty years ago, claims you look the same today as you did then.'

'That is perfectly true, Madame, I made the acquaintance of Countess de Gergy a long time ago.'

'But then you must be over one hundred years old.'

Not to be drawn he answered with a laugh, 'That is not impossible.'

'You gave Madame de Gergy an elixir with the most surprising of effects,' Madame Pompadour persisted. 'She claims that for quite a while she did not look older than twenty-four. Why don't you give some to the King?'

Saint Germain played shocked and explained with feigned indignation: 'But Madame, I would have to be totally mad, if I even *thought* of the idea of giving the King an unknown drug.' Saint Germain had first made acquaintance with King Louis XV and Madame Pompadour in 1749. Over the years, he cultivated a close friendship with them both, and frequently held long conversations with the king about alchemy and the extension of life.

At one such meeting the king made Saint Germain an attractive offer. 'If you find the elixir of life or the "stone of the wise men", we will be prepared to buy the formula. In the meantime we will put a chateau at your disposal and offer you a salary.'

At first the count insisted on paying the upkeep for the house himself, and as evidence of his wealth he gave Louis XV a handful of unformed diamonds which he carried in his deep, embroidered coat pocket. But the king insisted on providing him with the magnificent chateau of Chambord with its 440 rooms and installing an alchemist's laboratory for him there. The count lived there until 1760, then he travelled on further across Europe, firstly on a diplomatic mission to The Hague, then to London, where according to a report in the *London Chronicle* the following incident took place . . .

A duchess afraid of aging and its unavoidable signs, who was plagued by wrinkles and crowsfeet, had asked the Count to come and see her and after the usual pleasantries she asked his advice.

'Count, I have heard that you know the invaluable secret which restores youth. This medicine is said to be worth more than all your gold. Perhaps I don't need this preparation at the moment,' she flirted, 'but time passes only too quickly. Unfortunately! And so I thought to myself, a medication which can heal must surely also be preventative. As I would now like to undertake something before it is too late, I would ask you to let me have this preparation and name your terms.'

'Those who know a secret, do not attach importance to letting others profit from it,' the count replied, but seeing her crestfallen expression on her face he took pity. The next day he brought the duchess a phial, which contained about five spoonfuls of a liquid. He explained to her that she was to take ten drops each at full and at new moon. The preparation was harmless but irreplaceable. The duchess hid the little bottle carefully between her toiletry articles and left the house to visit a lady friend. During her absence her chambermaid suffered an attack of colic and searched through the house for a liqueur. Finally, she came across the well-hidden phial. She opened it, smelt it and concluded that it must certainly be something good. She tried it once, twice and, adoring its taste, drank the whole bottle.

The Dream

In the evening the duchess returned to her palace. She called her maid – and was astonished. 'But child, who are you?' she asked. 'Where are you from?'

'I have come to undress you for the night as I do every day. After all that is my duty as your maid, which I have been for many years.'

'Impossible!' The duchess smiled. 'My maid is forty-five years old and you are sixteen at the most!'

Meanwhile, the Count of Saint Germain had taken himself off to Russia via Germany. There he participated in the fall of the Russian Tsar, Peter III, in 1762 and helped Catherine the Great to the throne. In 1769, he visited Frederick the Great in Potsdam, then travelled on to Venice and finally back to Russia. From 1774 to 1776 he stayed in Triesdorf, then travelled to Leipzig, Dresden, Celle and Hamburg. On 23 October, 1778, a gentleman called Dresser wrote to Baron Uffel, a judge in Celle:

'I have to report some news to your Excellency about a phenomenon. A man, who calls himself Saint Germain and refuses to disclose his origin, is staying here in the Kaiserhof hotel. He is living in great style . . . He corresponds with the great crowned heads, but doesn't bother with society with the exception of Countess Bentick and the French ministers. It is very difficult to learn more about him. He is an amateur in natural science, he has studied nature; and thanks to this knowledge he is now 182 years old and looks like a man in his forties. He told me in the strictest confidence that he has certain pills at his disposal, with which he achieves all these results, including the mutation of metals . . .'

These pills were also mentioned by Casanova in his memoirs. He had met the Count during a serious illness. Saint Germain had given him fifteen pills and explained that he would be healthy again after fifteen days. And it happened just so.

In 1778, he called on his friend, the prince Carl of Hesse-Kassel, who provided him with an 'alchemy tower' in Louisenlund castle near Eckernförde. Apart from a few short trips away he stayed there until the supposed day of his death on 27 February, 1784. This date is recorded in the church book of Eckernförde as the day on which 'the so-called Count of Saint Germain and Weldon died and [was] buried quietly in the local church'.

Supposing he was actually forty-five years old, when he met Countess Gergy in Venice in 1708, then he must have been born in 1663 and must have been at least 121 years old at the time of his death. But this date is controversial, for one year later the count is named as one of the participants of the 'Great Meeting of the Congress of Freemasons in Wilhelmsbad' on 15 February, 1785. The Comtesse d'Adhemar also claims to have seen him on many occasions after 1784. She explains so in her work *Memories of Marie-Antoinette*:

'I saw Monsieur de Saint Germain to my indescribable surprise over and over again. In 1793 at the queen's execution; in 1804 the day after the death of the Duke of Enghien; in January 1813; and on the evening before the murder of the Duke of Berry in 1820.'

The mysterious wonder man would then have been at least 157 years old. Could it be that he is still among us today? Has he perhaps discovered the secret of eternal youth, the Methuselah Formula?

CHAPTER THREE

Of Quacks, Tricksters and Discoveries New

It's highly unlikely that we'll ever know the full truth about the antics of Saint Germain. Maybe some of his claims were dubious, maybe he *had* found a wonder cure-all – what we do know is he lived a very long time, and for most of it possessed an uncanny energy. If it weren't for documented accounts and a wealth of anecdotal evidence many might dismiss him as one of the numerous rogues, charlatans and quacks who thrived by the dozen from the Middle Ages up to Victorian times. For example, there were the sly foxes among the alchemists of the middle-ages who had a curious ability to discover the legendary stone of the wise men whenever there was a demand for it. And, distributing it piece for piece as an 'immortality pill' in return for copious quantities of money, there always seemed to be enough to go round. The travelling 'natural healers' of the 18th and 19th centuries behaved equally unscrupulously and were, as to be expected, forever a hairsbreadth ahead of the guardians of the law.

While some searched for immortality on far-off islands or in sources or waters which were impossible to locate, others believed that they could achieve it through careful living and self-discipline. The Chinese taoists aimed for 'the path to the basis of the world', seeking the prolongation of life by meditation, breathing techniques, special diets, gymnastics, and special sexual practices.

What we would consider as a conventionally scientific fight against aging probably began in the 16th century with Paracelsus, the Englishman Basil Valentine, the Franciscan monks and, in particular, the philosopher-cum-scientist Roger Bacon. He used reason as an instrument against the fear of death. Because the immortality of the soul was to him an indisputable fact, he also saw realistic possibilities of prolonging life. And as human life expectation had gradually decreased since Paradise, this had to be a process which could be totally or at least partly reversed. After all, if our ancestors lived to such a ripe old age, surely we could do the same?

Only too quickly did a number of business-minded 'representatives of immortality' sieze the chance to compete against Bacon with their own formulas. One such entrepreneur was Italian Luigi Cornaro who, by his own admission, had pursued a dissipated life of wanton excess until it caught up with him when he was only forty-five. Afflicted by gout, stomach cramps, bouts of fever and unquenched thirst — for whatever drink he could lay his hands on — he was obliged, on the sombre advice of his doctors, to drastically change his lifestyle or make his will. In panic, he abandoned all his favourite habits within an hour of this fateful meeting. From then on he became a model of abstinence. He worked out a special diet consisting of a little bread, hardly any meat, soup with egg and young wines, which suited him so well that even at the age of ninety he still possessed the mental faculties to look after his written work himself and it wasn't until the venerable age of 103 that he departed this life.

In the next two hundred years the ideas of Cornaro served time and again as a stimulus to the representatives of the various branches of scientific knowledge. The most important follower among them was the 18th-century doctor Christoph Wilhelm Hufeland, a friend of Goethe and Schiller. He was the first German doctor to carry out innoculations and was famous for developing a formula to determine a human being's maximum lifespan. According to his observations, the average life of many animals is eight times the length of time it takes to reach physical maturity from birth. So dogs take one to one and half years before they are fully grown, which corresponds with a life span of about eight to twelve years. If it's true of animals, why not us? According to Hufeland, humans are normally fully grown at the age of twenty-five and should therefore have a maximum life span of two hundred years. Just like Cornaro, Hufeland was also an advocate of a moderate way of life; however he expressly pointed out that a person who really wanted to live a long life must beware of the greatest adversaries . . . namely vicious dogs and suicide!

The founder proper of gerontology, however, must be the 19th-century medic Jean-Martin Charcot, who practiced at the Saltpetrière hospital in Paris. This institute derived its name from a former saltpetre factory, which had been turned into a nursing home for the old and needy. Charcot's friendly, understanding rapport with the aged led him to many new discoveries, which he published in 1867 in a work proclaiming the establishment of a new scientific field of research – gerontology. In it, he mainly dealt with the organic changes associated with aging.

Research continued apace and by the beginning of the 20th century, gerontology had become established as a major empirical science. Most of the quackery and positing of theories that could never be satisfactorily tested had disappeared. The emphasis now was visible results which could be clearly explained through cause and effect. However, some of the experiments performed under the banner of empiricism were not only dubious, but utterly eccentric.

Take Charles Brown-Séquard, for instance. This professor of medicine at the Collège de France disclosed to an audience of fascinated listeners made up of experts and laymen with an average age of seventy-one, how he had managed to rekindle his tiring virility by giving himself injections of animal scrotal extract. The scientist then described, in detail, his tests carried out over a period of over twenty years.

Ever since 1869, when Brown-Séquard had explained to his students at the Paris Faculté de Médecine, that the sexual performance of an old man could probably be revitalised by an injection of scrotal extract from an energetic animal, the thought of manufacturing a rejuvenating serum from gonads wouldn't leave his mind. The manufacturing process for this 'medicine' was however so repulsive that the reader should be spared the details. Anyway, Brown-Séquard injected the painstakingly and painfully manufactured canine scrotal extract into his leg. At first all that resulted was excrutiating tissue inflammations and persistent insomnia. The professor reported that before the first injection he had been so exhausted that he couldn't even work for half an hour without having to sit down inbetween. But on the following day he was incomparably better and from then on his health steadily stabilised.

Not suprisingly, many experts rigorously disputed Brown-Séquard's findings and implied he had suffered a 'senile slip-up'. In his defence, however, it must pointed out that the professor is to thank for the promotion of organ therapy and for his research into the body's production of internal fluids and secretions.

Whether his methods actually triggered a process of rejuvenation is not certain. If he did regain his vitality at all then it was certainly only for a short time. Later on, however, Brown-Séquard admitted he suspected his 'rejuvenation phase' could be attributed to a placebo effect.

His work wasn't unique. He followed in the footsteps of a long line of medics who, throughout history, believed illnesses and afflictions could be cured by using animal or even human organs and not necessarily through transplantation. At the beginning of the 16th century Paracelsus had already announced boldly that the kidney heals the kidney, the heart heals the heart, the liver heals the liver.

The Dream

Historically, this idea was old hat. In 1500 BC, the *Papyros Ebers*, a medical book of formulas, had shown how impotence could be cured with the help of bull's testicles. And in India the highly regarded surgeon, Susruta, recommended a drink made from the testicles of young tigers. Plinius the Elder, imperial and roman commander and writer living around 24 AD, recommended the testicles of young boars to tackle impotency and advised those suffering from a liver disorder to eat wolf's liver.

Of course there was a bitter rivalry among the 'therapists' at that time, denouncing the remedies of his colleagues as a competitor might slate a rival product. The Greek doctor and philosopher Claudius Galenos attacked his colleague Xenokrates, because he used 'revolting' parts of animals and humans, not least human liver and human skin, to make his cures.

In 77 AD, the Greek doctor Dioskorides wrote the first major medical textbook, the *Materia Medica* in which the healing power of animal organs was also covered. This book remained a major influence to doctors around the world for 1500 years and right through the Middle Ages it dominated medical practice and thought.

Age and virility and their effects on each other have been bed partners for many years in the field of gerontological research. Although a healthy man should retain his potency and fertility right up to an old age, difficulties with impotency were mainly interpreted as a sign of aging in a man, even as an essential part of the aging process. For the woman, her signs of aging were modestly ignored from the start.

Viennese physiologist Eugen Steinach (1861-1944) considered the visible signs of male aging extremely important. He proposed that separating the vas deferens from the testicles could stimulate the production of hormones, thus reviving the performance of older men.

Steinach, who in years of experiments with rats had proved the interaction between the gonads and general fertility, one day severed the vas deferens of an old rat and waited to see what would happen. He claimed that after the male rat had recovered from the operation it pounced on a female rat and didn't leave her alone, until it had proved its regained potency an impressive nineteen times in a period of fifteen minutes.

The severance of the spermatic cords, known as the vasoligature should theoretically stimulate the body to increase hormone production by blocking the production of sperm. Today this method is not used for 'rejuvenation', but for birth control worldwide.

During this time it seems that testicle transplant fever was sweeping the world. In the case of Serge Voronoff (1866-1951) the Russian surgeon living in France, donorship shifted from dog to monkey. As the former eunuch advisor to the Egyptian khedive Abbas II, he had collected urological experience worldwide and was seen as an expert on problems of potency. Voronoff declared at the beginning of the First World War, 'A man loses more than fertility when he loses his "treasures".' Only after the removing the testicles does it become clear how important the function of the inner glandular secretion is. All of the organs, and therefore the whole of the organism, rely upon a hormonal secretion in the gonads. There is a close connection between the aging process and the gonads.

An avalanche of excited speculation was triggered by the very successful transplantation of a monkey's thyroid gland into the nape of a mentally handicapped child. The harrowing drawings of the child before and after the operation were then exploited 'ad nauseam' in newspapers everywhere.

Voronoff made a killing, financially, and consequently spent the rest of his time and resources to investigating methods of rejuvenation. Noting the spectacular failures of some really very respected scientists, he decided not to fall back on the gonads of various kinds of animals, but to experiment exclusively with human gonads.

Convinced that his brilliant idea would be received everywhere with great enthusiasm, he advertised for volunteer donors. But the unthinkable happened and only two workers wanted to sacrifice their precious gonads to science — and then only for a comfortable pension for life. Outraged at what he considered the despicable avarice of both men, Voronoff did without their gonads. But he wasn't to be defeated. The next best thing to the human version would be anthropoid, i.e. human-like, testes. Monkeys abounded — not ideal, but at least a feasible temporary solution.

Unscrupulously, the surgeon sent European and African hunters after his precious game — orang-utans, chimpanzees and long-armed apes — offering large sums of cash. In doing so he has gained the dubious distinction of having started the greatest ape hunt of all time. Within a short time great hordes of African apes lived in the park of Voronoff's dream palace on the Riviera which he had adapted especially for them.

Of course, it was only the upper classes who could afford to have their gonads reconditioned with glandular stripes from apes to increase potency. The great maestro asked for 5000 dollars a time for his services, and that was the lower limit. With an estimated 2000 transplants Voronoff made a massive fortune, even by today's standards.

He was confident that his theories would work in practise. Indeed he promised his aged patients the unspoilt pleasure of six to ten years of extended youthfulness. As a precaution he let his patients know that possibly 15% of his transplants could be unsuccessful. This, of course, could always be portrayed positively: the remaining 85% felt so much better that the effects of his cure could last for years. That, at least, was the sales patter. The primary beneficiary of this strange remedy was, of course, the practitioner himself. Many of the patients didn't notice, returning regularly at two yearly intervals for the follow-up treatment, and paid up every time without batting an eye.

Understandably, his contemporaries were deeply disgusted. Shortly before his death Voronoff experienced his own personal catastrophe. The patients came back in droves, though not this time for more treatment. A long list of serious complaints. Since having his transplants, many patients had suffered terribly. And they knew exactly where they could lay the blame. Voronoff defended himself with all the arguments at his disposal. But in the end the similarities between cases were too great for him to deny. The patients had come to his clinic in good faith and the best of health, but with the transplant of ape testicles Voronoff had afflicted upon them one of the most degrading scourges known to the human race: syphilis!

The trade in potency was not limited to Europe. It boomed in the New World. For a man like John Romulus Brinkley, America really was a land of opportunity, and boy, did he embrace it. Today it seems totally incomprehensible how this testicle transplanter, who was worshipped by his supporters, could manage to palm off 6000 billy goat testicles, at a price of $750 each, to around 16 000 strict Puritans. But John Romulus affirmed that they were craving to have the much sought-after goat testicles applied little by little to their own testicles for absorption.

The American health authorities acted towards this awful therapy like the three wise monkeys – hear no evil, see no evil, speak no evil. That was not surprising, as the cunning adventurer courted the favour of dignitaries from both political parties ensuring he was able to carry out his trade undisturbed. Like Voronoff, however, time eventually caught up with him. After a demonstration of his testicle transplantation methods in front of the Kansas State Medical Registration Board he was forbidden to continue practicing what were considered despicable treatments. So he took himself and his clinic over the border to Mexico. There he reinstalled his own radio station 'XENT' and proceded to broadcast his promise of 'unbelievable sexual strength, the details of which can only be hinted at' over the airwaves and, naturally, back over the border. And they came, the potency hunters. From all corners of the United States they hurried, full of determination and high hopes, to Mexico, to let themselves be given billy goat testicles. In the long term John Romulus Brinkley was the only winner. For after all his operations, the only thing that stood up proud was his bank account, totalling a perfectly erect $12,000,000.

The first conference devoted exclusively to gerontology took place in Kiev in 1938. And the first published research on this topic appeared in 1939 in the Soviet

Union. The father of Russian gerontology, zoologist and bacteriologist, Ilja Metchnikov, was born in the Ukraine in 1845 and later emigrated to France. Until his death in 1916, he delivered lectures and teach-ins as a professor at the Institut Pasteur in Paris, covering the history of invertebrates, bacteria, and research into toxins and immunity. In 1908, he was awarded the Nobel Prize for his great discovery of phagocytosis, the digesting qualities of unicells, on which, among other things, the human immune system is based.

As Metchnikov, unlike many other gerontologists of his time, held that his science should seek rejuvenation in totality, he investigated everything which he believed stood in the way of humanity's right to a longer life, especially infectious diseases which could cut people down in their prime. To him, aging and premature death were unnatural processes. He protested against the opinion that the aging process was an inevitable physiological phenomenon, pointing out that we only consider it normal because everyone suffers from it. And here, suffer is a key word. Metchnikov truly believed that growing old was nothing more and nothing less than a chronic illness. An illness, admittedly, that was a fearsome opponent to cures. In this respect, he was a forerunner of many of the scientists working on the problem today.

Metchnikov saw potential proof of immortality in the behaviour of the unicells, which neither age or die, and sought to explain, and thus find a way of halting the death of the multi-cell. For this excellent scientist the large intestine was the key to the problem and thus the arch-enemy. He was sure that the aging process was triggered by the bacterial putrefaction processes which take place in the large intestine and slowly poison the bodily organs. Rather drastically, he recommended an operation to remove the offending article. Patients would also be advised to eat as much yoghurt as possible to counteract the organisms that were responsible for putrefaction.

As to be expected, Metchnikov's hypothetical idea of the dispensable large intestine was only too soon turned into cash by others, one of whom was the English surgeon Sir William Arbuthnot Lane. This excellent, if misguided, surgeon was himself plagued by constant constipation and when he came across Metchnikov's works, it seemed like a message sent from heaven.

Sir William Arbuthnot Lane now made it his life's work to free his patients from their constipation complaints. From 1903 to his demise in 1938 he not only published a fair amount of works about chronic intestine constipation, but also rid all the patients which he could get his hands on and who could afford to pay, of their constipated large intestine, with the greatest precision.

That, it appears, was not enough for the zealous doctor. His loathing of the organ took on comical proportions, as he now also charged all other possible undefinable symptoms to the account of the large intestine — even lachrymal sacs, rheumatic fever in children, gall-bladder trouble, cancerous growths. Whatever was wrong with the patient, the large intestine was the culprit and it would pay by extraction.

Unbelievably, most of the patients coped with this radical cure, and many were even in a better state of health after the operation. Metchnikov, asked for his opinion of Lane's antics, had no objection to the conversion of his theory into practice — though neither were prepared to put their bodies where their knives were and subject themselves as guinea-pigs.

Despite his obsession with the intestines, Metchnikov's major contribution to medical advancement was his discovery of phagocytes. During a holiday in Italy he had observed starfish lava under the microscope and had established that the starfish cells digested everything they came across while eating. The scientist saw a similarity in behaviour with that of white blood corpuscles, which also surround and neutralise all poisonous substances to protect the organism against illness and infection.

After intense study of these white blood corpuscles and their defence mechanisms, Metchnikov finally came up with his theory about the aging process. He discovered that the most important tissues, those dedicated to a special task (like the heart, lung, kidney and liver) wear out over time. In his opinion, these important cells are replaced by bindweb fibres, which are formed due to phagocytation. Through these observations he was the first to pinpoint the crucial link between phagocytes and inflammations and immunity deficiencies.

Although the founders of modern gerontology provided much valuable groundwork (and a fair few sniggers), the main breakthroughs came after the Second World War. And we should thank English Nobel prize winner Sir Peter Medawar for making this field of research as popular, and important, as it is today. For he was one of the first pioneers to link the behaviour of our genes with the decay of our bodies. His preparatory work paved the way for the thousands of scientists now following him in the headlong rush to find the key to eternal youth.

The
Reality

CHAPTER FOUR

Aging – The Habit of a Lifetime

We've looked at the obsession with everlasting life that has gripped humanity throughout the ages, spawning theories too numerous to count (most of them spurious), doctors crazy enough to grace any 'mad professor' B movie, and all too often unscrupulous con-artists preying on the dreams of everyday people. The next question must be: why do we have these dreams? Is it simply ego? The thought of going on for infinity is possibly the greatest power fantasy ever conceived. Or curiosity? Nearly everybody at some time must have wondered what it would be like to go back in time, to actually witness the history we have read about in dry textbooks. *To be there.* Now, we can't, and as far as we know probably never will, go back in time. But what of the future? The world is changing so fast now that it's almost impossible to picture with any confidence what it will be like in two, three hundred years time. If, however, we could increase our lifespan to such an age, we would live the future. Most people reading these sentences will consider it an absolute certainty that they won't be around to see the year 2100. It's the stuff of science fiction. Some, of course, might not want to.

Two potential explanations for humanity's fixation with immortality – ego, possibly, curiosity, certainly plays a part. But the main one must be fear. The great majority, given the choice, would rather stay young than grow old. Sounds obvious, but it points out an important distinction between living forever and staying young. More than anything it is age and illness we fear, not death. Avoiding death would be a nice by-product admittedly, but there would be no point to immortality if all you could do was sit in a chair watching your garden grow into a jungle. Which is not to imply that old age is intrinsically boring or frustrating. Many people live active, healthy existences right up to their nineties and beyond. That said, it is indisputable that most of us fear the infirmity associated with old age. Even if only sub-consciously, we mourn the passing of our youth. Experience comes with the years, but imagine having both . . .

We fear old age because the statistics show it brings illness and decay. As you grow old, you may not feel the effects of the following statistics, but it's a fact that you'll be adding to them.

Health problems increase in line with our age. The process of aging actually begins in early childhood when the myocardial cells, the nerve cells and the cells in the skeleton end their process of separation. Growth observed in late youth is exclusively due to single cells, which are still multiplying, although the total number of cells is already decreasing. Young people age the quickest. Depending on the individual, somewhere between the twentieth and fortieth year our degeneration reaches a plateau, but accelerates again with the advent of old age. Whether we want to believe it or not, even in the brain of a twenty year old 10 000 nerve cells die every day and they are never replaced.

From twenty onwards, deterioration becomes physically visible and it begins with the first wrinkles – usually in the most noticeable places like around the eyes. According to your point of view this can be considered positively or negatively. Looked at medically, however, there are no two ways about it – the tissue that makes up our skin is ever so slowly decaying. So what's wrong with a few smile lines you might say. I can tackle that with a few creams, and besides it makes me look mature. All true, but what's going on out of sight is of much greater importance. The number of pigment cells, those all important barriers which protect our skin against the sun's ultraviolet rays, decreases by between 10-20% per decade. Therefore which each year we clock up, the chances of us contracting skin cancer increases – a danger which is especially worrying considering the state of the ozone layer. The layers of our skin (the epidermis, the corium and the hypodermis) dry out and lose their elasticity. Fat deposits dwindle away and with it the skin's capability to regulate the body temperature. That is why older people feel the cold more, when the temperature is low, but can't cool down as quickly in the summer.

While our skin relentlessly defers to gravity, so too does the upper section of our body. Most people shorten by up to ten centimetres between the ages of forty-five and eighty-five, by which time we'll probably be suffering from osteoporosis, where the very substance of our bones becomes lighter and more fragile, decreasing in weight from the age of thirty by one percent annually. And if you do strenuous sport to keep you heart fit and your stomach flat, you re more likely to end up with arthritis, because the cartilage in your joints will be worn-out or inflamed.

It seems we can't win. Our resistance, strength and senses weaken year on year until the wheel of life finally grinds to a halt, which means, for most people in the developed world, somewhere between seventy and one hundred years. At the moment this is an undeniable fact. Nature offers no alternatives.

For those still not convinced, here are a few further details. Our muscle weight and corresponding strength decreases about 30% between the ages of thirty and ninety. Muscle tissue shrinks while layers of fat increase. The number of nerve fibres in a nerve tract decreases by 25%. And our brain, with an average weight of 1375 grammes, shrinks by 345 grammes to 1030 grammes. Usually our short-term memory deteriorates considerably with old age.

In the Waste Disposal Department, the workers begin to go on strike, demanding less productivity and making sure you pay more. The capacity of the bladder is reduced by up to half – you'll be going more often and with less warning. The liver clearly decreases its function as a filter with the years. Alcohol, contaminants of all kinds, as well as medicines, remain in the body for longer periods. The nephrons in our kidneys, which extract the poisonous substances from the blood, are reduced to almost half their number. This explains why over-indulgence in our younger years leads only to mild retribution, but come middle age the hangovers hit hard and keep hitting for a great deal longer.

As if that weren't enough, you can't taste your drink as well as you used to. A teenager has about 245 gustatory cells per papilla on the tongue. If you make it to ninety only one third of these will remain. And much as we might try to blur our senses through drink, old age does it better. The lenses in the eyes harden, causing greater difficulty in focusing (particularly close-up), and less light penetrates through to the retina because our pupils narrow. Therefore the retina of an eighty year old generally receives only a sixth of the light which falls on that of a twenty year old. Incidentally lens opacity is often associated with hardening, thus increasing the likelihood of cataracts. It must be pointed out that there is an accidental and happy by-product to all this. Those with short-sight often experience a limited self-correction of their sight in later years – a direct result of the lenses' increased rigidity.

As with the eyes, so too the ears. And, most importantly, the heart. As the muscles in the heart grow weaker, less and less blood is pumped through our veins. A thirty-year-old at rest manages 3.4 litres per minute, at the age of seventy this falls to 2.5 litres while the heart of a ninety-year-old only pumps half as much as that of a twenty year old. Not only does it do less, it takes longer to recover after exercise. This is partly because it's more susceptible to illnesses. In the course of your life all sorts of damage – alcohol, tobacco, diet, pollution, lack of exercise – is done and all sorts of contaminants are deposited in your body. A common complaint is the build-up of calcium and collagens which stiffen the artery walls, cause high blood pressure and impair the function of the heart. Even if we disregard external factors, that function is destined to become less effective anyway because the cardiac pacemaker cells which guarantee a regular, healthy heartbeat decline in number with the years. Exacerbating this decline is a fall in lung performance by 50%, due to a loss of strength in the muscles which move them. So just when the heart needs more oxygen because it's pumping more slowly, it is asked to increase its rate to cope with lungs working harder but taking in *less* oxygen.

What happens outside the body is hardly more encouraging. Those smile lines which we brushed off as signs of maturity were actually warning signs of what is to come. At fifty the skin on the cheeks is losing water and elasticity. The effect is deeper wrinkles, drooping jowls and sagging gullet. The only things that keep growing are those we don't want, like moles and creases – and hair. For men it's hair in the ears, hair dangling from your nose and sprouting on your shoulders and back. On your head? That would be too kind. Off it falls. Women's hair also thins and loses its sheen. And both sexes must accept that they're going to go grey sooner or later.

Our immune system, the biological shield critical to our well-being, also weakens. The steady drop in performance of the defensive forces of the organism starts at about the age of thirty. In old age only a quarter of our T-lymphocytes are left to fight invaders like flu. In addition, at about the age of fifty years the thymus gland, the main gland in the immune system, recedes until it becomes almost invisible, increasing suscepti- bility to illness and decreasing ability to recover. A weakened defence force also raises the chance of cancer.

The nervous system doesn't escape scot-free either. Our reaction times are longer because the impulses sent from our brain through the nerve fibres travel at half the speed they did when we were children.

Everything in our body seems to slow down, and every day we die a little.

Of course, old age does not *equal* illness, frailness and senility like some cold mathematical equation. Far from it. Some people never visit a doctor in their lives. You can be picking up your OAP bus pass one minute and jogging around the local sports track the next, while someone a quarter your age could be wheezing their way up a three-step flight of stairs . . . if you've looked after yourself and reserved a fair slice of luck from the pie. The long list of ailments previously listed is not intended to create a stigma or horror at the prospect of becoming elderly. It is rather offered as an indication as to why the scientific community and the public at large is so fascinated with achieving the impossible – eternal youth. Make no mistake, com- pared to our potential (a potential that is about to be unleashed by advances in genetic engineering), the life span of human beings is tragically short.

Why that is so, is the fundamental question that scientists have been trying to solve for centuries. One area they look to for answers is in parts of our body that live on and work well, despite old age. Some of our most vital organs, like the heart, *can* compensate for their unavoidable signs of wearing by more economic use. If the heart escapes acute illness, several changes related to old age cannot prevent it from fulfilling its essential task of pumping blood through the veins in a perfectly satisfactory manner.

The same applies to the brain. Though it shrinks and cells are lost, it by no means gets worn out, and for most of our lives the loss is bearable. Compared to most of the other body cells, which are usually replaced after dying off, there is no replacement for dead brain cells. As seen earlier, this can mean the older brain is up to fifteen percent lighter. This depletion does lead to reduced performance but it doesn't mean that old people cannot master mental tasks as well as young people. They may need a little longer but this organic handicap is more than offset by a distinct social advantage – decades of experience when solving problems. It is not without reason that scholars often reach the high point of their achievements when others are applying for their pension.

For some things, there are no age limits. The idea that age and libido are incompatible is simply not true. An older man may need a little longer to get an erection but the level of testosterone coursing through his body is the same as when he was a teenager. There are many examples of men fathering healthy children in old age. Charlie Chaplin managed it without falling over. If an old man in good health becomes impotent it's more likely to caused by psychological factors than age. Women, similarly, can stay sexually active all their lives. If they suffer from physical complaints, such as hot flushes or vaginal dryness, these can often be eased by hormone replacement therapy. Indeed, after the menopause (the change of life) many women often experience an increased sex drive.

It must also be pointed out that, despite the statistics given earlier, an aging immune system does not lead directly to a permanent general decline of strength. Newer studies actually show that the capability of bone marrow to produce T-cells — cells, which themselves produce defensive substances to fight diseases — is not influenced by age. Whilst they don't adequately cover the loss of T-lymphocytes, T-cells have been an area of intense scientific interest and recent sensational experiments have indicated the possibility of counteracting this inadequacy in various ways.

All in all, we fear the finality of death but what worries us most is the loss of youth, our ability to do the things we used to. Some of these fears, as we have seen, are unfounded, some cannot be ignored. We can grow old gracefully and in good health if we don't abuse our bodies too much. But if we follow the Methuselah Formula we can grow old *and* stay young.

Our optimism as well as our capacity for enthusiasm are based on a simple biological fact: between our actual life expectancy, (the number of years we actually live) and our theoretical life span (the maximum number of years we can reach if nothing comes along in between), lies a huge gulf. But it is a gulf we are crossing bit by bit with every age-related discovery made.

About 2000 years ago, people reached an average age of only twenty-two years. In the Middle Ages it was twenty-five years, in the 18th century twenty-nine, in the 19th century forty-five and today life expectancy in industrial countries has reached an average of seventy-five years, with women enjoying a slight lead in the life-expectancy tables. By the end of the 20th century alone we will have increased our life expectancy by 60% – an advance for which we must thank, not least, the discovery of antibiotics.

Our life span, the absolute limit which only a very few reach has, however, remained the same. Increased life expectancy does not push up the life span. The latter is dictated by a gene program inherent in every one of us. Even if reports constantly appear about the supposed 'oldest person in the world' who still enjoys the best of health at the age of 130 or even 160 years, experts still assume that the maximum life span of man is about 115 years.

As the English gerontologist Dr. Comfort has proved in nutritional experiments with rats, 'the clock, which determines changes in age can be stopped, re-started and even slowed down.'

The main problem though lies in the discovery of the components which are responsible for the temporal course of events in the program of life. Do we become older, because various irreplaceable cells die? Are the cells manufactured in later years inferior to those in the earlier stages of life? Or do both of these factors, in conjunction with others unknown, play a role?

Comfort says: 'Many of the tissue characteristics typical for age such as lines, loose skin, hardened arteries and many more, can be traced back to the changes in the collagen (bindweb glue) in the tissue. For example, changes of this kind become apparent when looking at the differences in the tissue structure of a young crispy chicken and a tough, old boiling fowl.

On the other hand some cells, like those found in cartilage, hardly change during the course of life and can even survive death by many hours.

Not only are a series of secondary symptoms linked to the path to death, but this way is almost always complicated by illness. And some changes due to aging, such as those in the blood vessels, have follow-on and cumulative effects, causing disproportional damage when compared to the original problem.

The real problem, however, is that human beings have always killed themselves prematurely due to sociological, psychological and nutritional burdens. It is totally beyond doubt that the aging process is influenced by the demands of affluent society, by smoking, stress, pollution, agitation and even boredom.

From a physiological point of view, the aging process in humans progresses at different speeds. Even organs from the same body age at different rates. Dr. N. J. Berril of the McGill university in Montreal, Canada, made the following comparison 'If a man has twenty-six candles on his birthday cake, his heart and his muscles can nevertheless be as old as those of a man of thirty, his arteries can be forty, but his brain might only be nineteen.'

Most of us have friends or acquaintances in their thirties. In relation to their appearance and behaviour many of them could already be dragging half a century around with them on their hanging shoulders. On the other hand you may know of sixty-year-olds who can still make a night of it without a second thought and go about their work the next morning without any ill-effects whatsoever.

Men and women can go grey at any age between twenty and sixty. This confirms the claims of several gerontologists that there is no fixed point for the setting in of old age. There can be no fixed point because there are so many variables involved. Biological clocks, programs in our DNA, nutrition and mental attitude all play their part. The following chapters explore the effects of all these factors and the research which aims to eradicate them.

CHAPTER FIVE

Descendants of the Shamans

The human race has always been at the receiving end of pestilence, disease and chronic injury. Evidence has been recovered from as far back as the Stone Age which indicates tribes attempted a primitive, though intuitive, kind of accident surgery. Fractures were seen to, dressings were applied and wounds were sewn. Skulls recovered by archaeologists from the Neolithic period show precise circular incisions. It is believed these were surgical operations aimed at relieving various illnesses.

Later on patients were treated with laxative and pain-killing preparations, as well as with drugs such as hemp and opium to increase perspiration and thus rid the body of its affliction. Bleeding, the application of the cupping glass and other methods were used to withdraw blood for the same reason. These techniques were based on trial-and-error experience. It was some time before they were surpassed as inquiring minds started to question the reasons for illness.

The first phase was the development of the Foreign Body Theory. The illness was considered as an independent being which had forced its way into humans intent on malevolent work. Magical, demonic powers, which our ancestors believed lurked everywhere, were behind these deeds. Thus medicine became inextricably tangled with religion and mysticism. The experienced healer, who knew what to do but didn't know why, was now replaced by a medicine man or priest shrouded in mystery, who claimed the only way to heal suffering was by banishing the demons through exorcism. The idea of a 'conjured-up' illness and the personification of the foreign body were typical of the obsession and delusion. In many religions, illness meant a punishment or test of the gods, which was treated with ritual remedies and theurgy (the heathen art of magical exorcism of the gods).

Early on in the history of humankind, a caste of medicine men and shamans developed and spread throughout the world. These people held a revered place in society and were responsible for healing the sick through rituals and knowledge passed down through the family line. Concrete ideas about illness, death and life after were central components of shamanism. Many of these ideas became the basis of all mythology, religion and ultimately medicine. Even today shamanistic treatments are still performed in some countries. Naturally, they are in sharp contrast to the therapy used in modern medicine.

Descendants of the Shamans

The shaman's main function is to act as mediator between the spirits, the soul of the deceased and the souls of the other members of the tribe. In this guise – as a sorcerer-priest – he or she also takes on the role of the doctor. In Native American tribal groups when the shaman goes to a sick person, he wears special garments; a long loincloth, strips of leather and cloth, a decoration of threads which cover his face, bells and jangling metal pendants, and sometimes an additional head decoration. In Siberian and eskimo communities the shaman uses a tambourine or a drum and, with a cult chanting in accompaniment, slowly builds himself up into a state of frenzy in order to establish contact with the spirits.

Shamanism first and foremost recognises two kinds of illnesses: those which are due to foreign entities forcing themselves into the patient and those which involve the loss of the soul. Each has an entirely different method of treatment. In the first case, the evil caused by the illness must be driven out and in the second case the fugitive soul of the sick person has to be captured and returned to its rightful home. No-one apart from the shaman is capable of this, as only he or she has the gift of recognising souls and trapping them.

Even amongst the tribal groups of North America where there are shamans as well as medicine men, only the shaman can carry out the treatment of an illness which is caused by the loss of the soul. For only the shaman can command those helpful spirits, which investigate the cause of the illness, while sinking into a deep trance. This is why a shaman session always contains exorcism.

The sessions take place at night, usually in the dwelling of the sick person. During this ritual both the patient and the shaman must keep to certain rules. It is absolutely imperative that all 'impurities' are avoided – women who are menstruating or are pregnant fall into this category – and meat and salted food must not be eaten. The shaman uses an emetic to radically clean his body. Early in the morning he takes a bath, in order to sink into mediation and prayer at nightfall.

The actual treatment of the patient begins with a few questions. The shaman would like to know what the patient did in the period before the illness. From the response he ascertains why the illness has materialized. Then he gives instructions for a three to four metre long willow stick to be cut and its tip to be decorated with an eagle feather. He puts it by the patient's head, where it remains overnight. The eagle feather has special significance for native North Americans, symbolising the magical flight of the spirit.

Mid-evening the shaman visits the patient. He is accompanied by an interpreter, known as the 'speaker', whose task is to repeat all the shaman's mumbled words out loud. The interpreter says a prayer and then informs the patient him of the shaman's arrival. Throughout the proceedings the shaman is summoned intermittently and, according to an established ritual, asked to heal the sick person.

The shaman approaches the patient barefoot, his upper body naked, his voice singing quietly. The people present, who remain against the walls, repeat the shaman's improvised verses with the help of the interpreter. The inspiration to sing comes from the very depths of the unconsciousness and helps to call the assisting spirits. The shaman falls into such a deep trance that at the end of the session he cannot remember anything that has happened.

Descendants of the Shamans

The shaman rises and circles around a fire burning in the middle of the room. Then he retires to his seat, lights a pipe and takes a few puffs, before passing it on to the others assembled. The pipe does its round and on-lookers continue singing.

What happens next depends on the illness. If the patient is unconscious, this is certain proof of the loss of the soul. Now the shaman, who is still deep in self-hypnosis, must make a diagnosis and determine the treatment with his powers. Only an experienced practitioner can do this.

Images appear through the haze of the shaman's reverie, revealing cryptically or explicitly the cause of the illness. Finally, he awakes from his trance still singing and murmuring. When he has fully regained consciousness, he gives the persons present information about the patient's disorder in a very long-winded explanation.

If it is a magical foreign body, which has penetrated the sufferer, then the shaman tries to remove it. He sucks the part of the body where the focus of the sickness is. Many shamans use a bone or a tube made of willow for this. Accompanied by the singing of the people present and the interpreter, the operation takes its course until the shaman energetically rings the bell. He spits out the sucked blood into a previously prepared hole, takes a few puffs of the pipe, dances around the fire again and sucks the focus of the illnesses out once again, until the magical object – an insect, a worm, a lizard, a little stone – has been drawn out of the afflicted person. Triumphantly, he displays the visible proof of his successful treatment to all, then throws it into the little hole and fills it with dust.

The singing and the smoking ceremonies carry on until midnight, then a meal follows according to the

shaman's instructions, though he himself doesn't parti-
cipate. Only at the break of day does the ritual finish.
Shortly before it does, the shaman asks those present to
dance and sing around the fire with him for about a
quarter of an hour. Then he gives the patient's relatives
instructions as regards diet and explains to them which
signs must be painted on his body to help ensure future
good health.

Scientific practices evolved from magic ritual. About
4000 years ago in China, a relatively sophisticated
pharmaceutical and medical literature existed in the
form of writings on bamboo tablets. As well as indi-
cations, these tablets listed suitable drugs and their
proportions in prescriptions; that is to say a precise
dose as well as the suitable form of medicine. Treatment with medicinal herbs played an important role,
and still does today.

Around 1500 years later the 'humoral' theory
developed in Greece, shaping medicine for the next
millennium. It was the baby of Empedocles (490 BC), a
very popular and widely admired philosopher but it was
Hippocrates of Cos (around 460-375 BC), the great
Greek physician, who ensured its stature by applying
the hypothesis to medicine.

According to the humoral theory, which is derived
from the four basic qualities cold, warmth, dryness and
moisture, the elements are formed by the combination
of pairs of properties such as: dryness and cold = earth;
warmth and moisture = air; cold and moisture = water;
dryness and warmth = fire.

A collection of medical tracts, which go back as far
as Hippocrates, also contains the book about the nature
of man. To all appearances this is the first time that the

four human bodily fluids were mentioned and systematically registered. These four 'cardinal fluids' – blood, mucus, dark and light bile – are considered in the text to be the carriers of life. Their fundamental qualities correspond to the four elements – earth, water, air and fire. If these four fluids are in the right proportions, then good health is assured. But every divergence brings an illness with it.

As Hippocrates came from an old-established family of physicians, secret knowledge was traditionally passed down from father to son. These principles and diagnoses, however, originally came from the Babylonians and Egyptians, who had literally set their findings in stone in the form of temple drawings. These temples were dedicated to Asclepius, the god of medicine, and the most famous ones were in Cos, Epidauros, Rome, Pergamum and Athens. Sick people flocked to these cities, desperate to learn remedies that might cure them.

Hippocrates, however, was not content to rest on the laurels of his predecessors. He had his own doctrines to pursue. One of which was that human health was influenced decisively by the environment. This outstanding physician combined incisive scientific thinking, a brilliant talent for observation and high morals. In his temples, patients were subject to a strongly suggestive atmosphere, which encouraged convalescence. Here, the routine was strict, and had the sole objective of healing. Baths, diets, ban on alcohol, sacrifices and religious rituals were established in the name of healthy living.

Claudius Galen (129-199 AD), the most famous physician of the antiquity after Hippocrates, took to the theory of bodily fluids enthusiastically and pushed it further. He combined all the knowledge from antique medicine to devise a complete and logical system that became the yardstick for healers right up to the beginning of the modern era. After codifying his knowledge he went on to combine the humoral theory with a special pneuma or breathing theory, according to which the matter contained in the air we breathe was a carrier of life. Its poison was therefore considered to be the essence of all illnesses.

In his younger years Galen, had received a comprehensive philosophical education, and after that he studied medicine in Pergamum, Smyrna, Corinth and Alexandria. In 158 AD he returned to his home town to look after wounded gladiators. A few years later he went to Rome where, from 164 AD he practiced with great success, gaining an excellent reputation from his public lectures on the anatomy. Rome was however so spoilt for him by the attacks of jealous rivals that after only three years he turned his back on the city.

Galen then went on research trips through Greece and Asia, until he finally returned back to his home town, Pergamum. But he didn't stay here for long either, as he was soon summoned to Rome by the emperor Marcus Aurelius. There he eventually died at the age of seventy, highly respected by his contemporaries, envied by his lessers.

Between the Roman era and the Middle Ages medical progress was slow, if not stagnant. As modern chemistry gained ground, the theory of bodily fluids entered a new stage. The natural scientist and physician Paracelsus (1493-1541), or to be more exact, Theophrastus von Hohenheim, replaced the four fluids in this theory with three chemical principals – salt, mercury and sulphur – as symbols of the substances and forces which he believed formed the living substratum of the body. In some respects, Paracelsus must be seen as the founder of chemotherapy as he increasingly added minerals, and some understanding of what they do, to our fund of medicines

At the beginning of the twentieth century the way was then paved for greater synthesis of knowledge in all areas of science: physics, chemistry, bacteriology, hormone theory and last but not least psychosomatic medicine, all played on each other resulting in many innovations and insights. Methods of examination and treatment, such as electrodiagnosis, X-ray diagnosis and serological examination methods were products of such marriage of the sciences. Pharmacological experiments created new medicines, including sulphonamide and antibiotics, which had a profound influence on the lives of millions of people.

Despite all these advances, the human body is still far from indestructible. Although the medics have the most modern computers at their disposal for making an analysis and diagnosis, although there are revolutionary examination procedures, like scintigraphy in nuclear medicine – the localizing of diagnostics using radionuclides – and although the pharmaceutical industry comes up with new drugs almost every day, conditions such as cancer, heart disease and diabetes, among a host of others, are still not guaranteed curable.

That's the situation as it stands today. But perhaps it paints a misleadingly bleak picture. The prospects for future cancer suffers are looking brighter all the time. Recent research has led to a flurry of activity concentrating on the link between cancerous growths and viruses. It has now been proved that certain types of virus act as triggers. They smuggle themselves into healthy cells, reprogramming the occupied cell with their own DNA commands. If the patient has a strong defensive system, the intruder is isolated by the body's police force, the white blood corpuscles, and is therefore put out of action. But if the police force is depleted, through aging, environmental influences or other circumstances, it is possible for the disguised nucleinic acid of the intruding virus to send commands for continual cell division – letting the cancer run riot.

Up to now malignant tumours have been removed by an operation, irradiated (a process in which the tumour is burned out) or treated with a concentrated course of chemicals. None of these methods is foolproof. And, unfortunately, side effects and relapses are still quite common. For there is never an absolute certainty that every last cancer cell has been destroyed. Toxins are often left as by-products of radio or chemotherapy and can impair the function of the body's organs. All medicines which are presently used to treat cancer are supposed to prevent cell division, and to therefore stop the growth of the tumour. But so far, these drugs have been unable to differentiate between healthy and cancerous cells.

Scientists have, however, come across a trick whereby a virus smuggles its hereditary information into a foreign cell, using an enzyme's reverse transcriptase. This substance, which is a typical 'aiding substance' for cancer produced by viruses has been isolated in human cancer tumours. One of the main aims of cancer research at the moment is to find a means of freeing the cancer sufferer of the virus' own Reverse Transcriptase Enzymes.

The first thing these enzymes do in a cell occupied by cancer viruses is to attack the cell walls, forming new proteins. The immune system tries to repel these foreign substances – as they would after the transplantation of a foreign organ – often with little success, for the cancer cells are masked by a substance which misleads the lymphocytes (a special type of white blood corpuscle) thus protecting them from attack.

This knowledge led to a series of tests involving dogs with breast cancer. Professor H.G. Schwick from the Behring company in Marburg, Germany, removed tumour tissue from the affected area and proceeded to break it down into single cells. He then subjected these to a 'neuraminidase wash' and injected the tissue back into the sick dog. Thus treated, the cancer cells' masks were removed. Exposed, they could no longer repulse the antibodies and were quickly destroyed. The cancerous lump in the dog's breast dissolved. Overall, the tests had a 90% success rate.

Meanwhile, research laboratories are busy developing an ambitious program for a vaccination which will prevent the cancer viruses from penetrating the body in the first place. Dr. Maurice Hillemann, director of virus research at the Merck Institute in West Point, USA, is another convinced that cancer is caused by viruses and that it must therefore be possible to fight it with a virus vaccination. A series of animal experiments have meanwhile shown that anti-cancer vaccinations have been successfully tested. For their tests in Göttingen, Germany the researchers Professor R. Laufs and Dr. H. Steinke used primates closely related to man – crested bare-faced tamarins – who had developed lymphatic cancer. From the virus Herpes saimiri, which does not occur in man, the researchers manufactured a vaccination by killing off the cancer causing agents. The tamarins were injected with this vaccination and subsequently infected with cancer. The vaccinated animals were all still alive after two years without the slightest signs of illness.

There are other weapons in the fight against cancer: microscopically small latex globules coated with suitable antibodies are able to detect certain types of cancer cells and destroy them. Dr. Alan Rembaum from the California Institute of Technology is hoping that during the course of further tests, these 'fighting globules' can be further developed into highly sophisticated carriers, which can transport medicines or radioactive elements, in order to attack and eliminate cancerous and other undesired cells while leaving the rest of the body intact.

Back across the Atlantic in Sweden, scientist Dr. Bertil Bjorklund developed a simple blood test to identify cancer some years ago. This 'TPA' diagnosis equipment works according to the same principles as the already well-known tests for measles, mumps or smallpox. A blood sample is tested for a certain kind of antigen known as a polypeptide (a substance which causes the formation of antigens). Dr. Bjorklund, Director of the Cancer Immunology Section at the National Bacteriological Laboratory, isolated this antigen and discovered that it is very often found in connection with malignant tumours.

Revolutionary innovations are also being prepared in other fields of medicine. Laboratory animals have received atomically powered artificial hearts. This is the first time that scientists have managed to manufacture artificial hearts which are fully functionable as an integral part of the organism. Experiments with such hearts were carried out on behalf of the American National Institute of Health by the Thermo Electron

Corporation together with the Harvard Medical School. In most industrial countries, heart failure claims a massive number of victims. In the USA alone the annual toll is a staggering 200 000 people and that figure doesn't include those who are badly disabled after an attack or those who die early due to heart disease or related surgery. So the potential for life-saving from the availability of an artificial heart that actually works and *keeps* working is enormous.

Heart research may be relatively young, but is has made great strides in a very short time. The first mile-stone was set in 1967 with the successful implantation of a blood pump into a laboratory animal. The heart is basically a two pump system. The right-hand ventricle pumps the blood with little pressure into the lungs, where carbon dioxide is released and oxygen is absorbed. The left-hand ventricle pumps the blood, enriched with oxygen, into the arteries with a high level of pressure.

Most heart attacks occur due to left ventricle failure, as this side has to work four times as hard as the right. Early investigations therefore concentrated on develop-ing the artificial heart on the left-hand side of the heart; this lead to the construction of a booster pump between the left-hand side of the heart and the aorta. With the further development of heart research, booster pumps were then connected to both heart ventricles.

In a system which is undergoing tests at the moment, an artificial heart is powered by a plutonium 238 capsule. The next step will be a fully implanted artificial heart, controlled by a microcomputer no bigger than a penny. Lowell T. Harmison, from the American National Heart and Lung Institute, is of the opinion that the development of such a heart is no less a challenge than the Apollo moon project. The technical requirements demand nano-technology — an extremely painstaking miniaturising of the components.

Due to the obvious risks of rejection, the surface material of an artificial heart is crucially important. Scientists have tried to outwit the body's defense mechanisms, sometimes in drastic ways. Today, the preferred method is to weaken the defensive system with chemical preparations. With alarming success. These preparations, in effect, paralyse the whole immune system of the organism. The patient has a chance of keeping his transplanted organ, but viruses, bacteria and fungi consequently have free reign. A variety of preparations, most of which stem cell division, are now supposed to positively influence the susceptibility of the patient. Although, the dangerous side-effects of these preparations would first of all have to be eliminated.

Strangely, an artificial heart does not provoke an immune reaction, and because of this it is seen as an important stride in donor technology — the first possibility of completely avoiding host rejection. (Natural heart transplants are often attacked mercilessly by the immune system.) There are still problems, however, blood tends to clot when coming into contact with non-organic material. To avoid such complications, research has turned to biological materials, similar to tanned leather, which are less likely to cause coagulation.

Even with all the inherent difficulties, the outlook for sufferers remains good. Most of the hurdles have been overcome, so hopefully, artificial human hearts will be available in only a few years time.

From the artificial heart to the pancreas. Many

millions of people in the world suffer from diabetes. When the pancreas malfunctions or closes down completely, the amount of insulin released – which regulates blood sugar – is reduced and in some cases halted altogether. If left untreated, diabetics run the risk of blindness, liver and renal failure, convulsions (known as 'hypos') or of falling into a deep state of unconsciousness due to their blood sugar level being either too high or too low. Artificial insulin, often extracted from a pig's pancreas, is now commonplace and because of this the condition is rarely life threatening and many diabetics live long healthy lives. However, the demands placed on the diabetic can be extreme. A constant awareness of how much sugar you've eaten compared with how much insulin you've injected (or ingested) is essential to stay healthy. Strenuous exercise makes the equation even more complicated.

An artificial pancreas now promises to make life much easier. The sugar control unit – a small disc about the size of a penny – was developed as early as 1972 in a joint project by the Joslin Diabetes Foundation in Boston, USA and the Whittaker Corporation Space Sciences Division. Recent improvements to this breakthrough device mean it could soon be widely available to diabetics around the world. The disc consists of two parts. One section continually controls the blood sugar level of the organism, while the other section intervenes with a dose of insulin, released through a micro-pump, as soon as the blood sugar level increases.

Scientists are firmly convinced that the sugar sensor disc is a major aid to diabetics. It is basically an energy cell producing a weak current, the intensity of which varies according to the amount of sugar in the tissue water. This sensor, which is implanted under the skin or in the peritoneal cavity, can be connected to a digital counter, with which the patient can check his blood sugar level from time to time. If the blood sugar level is low, a nutritional substance enriched with sugar can take remedial action. If the sensor disc shows too much blood sugar, then the pump automatically releases insulin. The micro-pump is very small, so it can be easily implanted into the body. And since the sensor disc is not powered by a conventional battery, but by a tiny nuclear unit, it will work indefinitely.

In the meantime, genetically reprogrammed micro-organisms or bacteria – which are equipped with the genes of plants, animals or even humans – are already able to take over the production of biological substances, of medicines, or of chemical substances in biological production plants. In this way bacteria can help to heal blood diseases and hereditary illnesses. Insulin can be grown with them and utilized industrially in bacterial cultures. Cows and pigs, who have up to now been the producers of insulin, would thereby be redundant – especially so, since bacteria are a lot cheaper to keep.

The process is extremely simple. A particular gene, which is produced in the insulin of rats, is introduced into the E.-coli bacteria. This gene is accepted by a few bacteria and duplicates with every cell division. And so, within a matter of a few hours, a small number of coli bacteria with a foreign genotype produce billions of copies. To indicate how much progress has been made, consider the following: in 1977, American scientists managed to isolate only a tiny trace, one five thousandth of a gramme of somatostatin from one hundred grammes of genetically altered coli bacteria.

And twenty years ago scientists needed the cerebral matter of 500 000 sheep to produce the same amount of this life-saving hormone.

Under the patronage of the Brookhaven National Laboratory in Upton, New York, an international team of researchers developed a tiny device in which human blood corpuscles can be reproduced and observed outside the body. A diffusion chamber with circular filters is filled with an exactly measured amount of human bone marrow and peripheral blood. Then this chamber is implanted into the peritoneal cavity of a living mouse. The chamber replenishes the red and white blood corpuscles in the same way as the bone marrow in the human body. Its bone marrow is maintained by the filtered substances in the mouse's blood, identical to those in human blood. Human blood cells have in this way already been derived from rabbits and goats.

The diffusion chamber system allows an insight into the complex details of the blood count in healthy as well as sick people. Due to this invention, important knowledge about a certain kind of leukaemia, caused by malfunctions in the metabolism, has been obtained. The system also has the major benefit of enabling comprehensive tests for new drugs in the fight against blood diseases to be made without having to use a human as a guinea pig.

Artificial organs, using micro-computers and tiny pumps, are one way forward. However, the next step will be perfectly copied organs, grown in cultures. There are a large number of lower forms of animal that are able to regenerate lost limbs. If, for example, a lobster loses a leg, then the base for a new limb is soon formed, from which a fully functioning leg develops in a short time.

The Reality

The biophysicist and surgeon Dr. Robert Otto Becker has devoted much of his scientific life to investigating regeneration. He became particularly interested after learning of the respected natural scientist Lazzaro Spallanzani's work conducted over two hundred years ago. Spallazani observed to his immense surprise that, when required, salamanders (from the amphibian family) could renew all parts of their body without difficulty, if necessary all at the same time and up to six times in three months.

When Becker delved deeper into these astonishing revelations he found that salamanders used two ingenious tricks to regenerate themselves. An extra-ordinarily 'weak wound' current flows into the nerves of the mutilated limbs. It is hard to believe, but it actually transforms specialised cells back into embryo cells from which all life is formed. With the help of newly stimulated growth hormones, muscle, nerve, bone and cartilage cells re-formed themselves.

Becker decided to stretch these findings to their logical limit. He tried an experiment with the halved heart of a salamander. To his amazement, it renewed itself within only eight hours. Elsewhere he found evidence of remarkable capabilities for regeneration within the natural world. Polyps, for example, are real geniuses at it. However many times one is dissected, each piece grows back into a complete version of its former segment. If the head is split in half, then two new heads are formed from the halves. It seems their ability for renewal is unlimited. According to Becker such processes must in principle also be possible in mammals, not least in humans.

Dr. Becker modified this technique and tried it on white rats, whose forelegs had been amputated. In most cases the tissue of the laboratory animals was regenerated. The new leg had the same cellular structure as a normal one and also the same complexion. Bones, cartilages, marrow, muscles and the blood vessels had all been renewed, if not completely.

Similar methods were then used on human fractures which would not heal because of bone marrow inflammation. Dr. Becker laid silver wires in some of his affected patients. The wires conducted low electric currents. Genetically engineered growth hormones were introduced. In addition a silver nerve fibre was implanted to give off silver ions which would kill bacteria and stem any inflammation.

According to Dr. Becker the results of these various experiments are so convincing that their importance for the human race cannot be underestimated. A perfection of this technique in, for example, heart muscles which have stopped working due to the failure of the coronary vessels, offers incredible prospects for increased longevity and well-being. Becker is convinced that one day it will be possible for all organs, limbs, bones – in fact, *any* part of our body – to be regrown. His opinion is shared by many other researchers who are working with recently discovered growth hormones that could actively influence the regeneration abilities of our bodies.

Everywhere revolutionary innovations are in sight. Even a traditional diagnosis from your GP will be affected. The day is no longer so far away when we will visit the doctor without actually seeing him face to face – at least not until we have explained our problems to his computer.

Medics at the University of Wisconsin took some convincing that their computer was equal to the tasks set for it. But it passed with flying colours, analyzing a patient's medical history and preparing diagnostic reports without fault. Compared to physicians, the computers can now provide a more comprehensive overview of a patient's state of health. It has a vast access to information and can process it near instantly. And it has the added advantage of a computer printout – a vast improvement on most doctors' illegible scribbles.

Specifically, the new approach works like this. During the interview, carried out by computer, questions regarding the patient's state of health appear on the screen. The patient answers by pressing a key with either – 'Yes', 'No', 'Not known' or 'Not understood'. If the patient's health is obviously in danger, the computer asks additional questions. According to the scientists at the University of Wisconsin the computer diagnosis is more reliable than that of the physician. Even if the computer is not able to replace the doctor-patient relationship, which is clearly essential, it can at least take some of the load off the increasingly overworked doctors. The massive amount of data stored by the computer, coupled with easy access is also a reliable failsafe against oversight and misdiagnosis.

Taken together, these rapid advancements in genetic engineering, biotechnology, computer science and medicine point to a considerable extension of life in the not too distant future. An astonishingly large number of Americans have so much confidence in medical progress that they have themselves frozen immediately after their death, with instructions to be revived as soon as medical technology enables. Under promising company names such as 'Alcor Life Extension

Foundation' or 'Transtime', the deceased are 'buried' in high-grade steel tanks filled with liquid nitrogen. And there they will remain preserved at a temperature of − 196C − defying time and embracing hope.

The American Cryonics Society in Silicon Valley, California, has two hundred members and is enjoying a steady rise in popularity. Similar groups have sprung up all over the USA. Several clever businessmen have got in on the act knowing that where there's a wish, there's a way − of making dollars. Take insurance agent Irving Rand from Long Island as an example. He devised the ingenious idea of issuing insurance policies for those wishing to be frozen. The insurance sum of 500 000 dollars includes 125 000 dollars for the preparation and storage of the corpse. The insured person 'receives' the rest after his 'resurrection' as an initial aid for a 'new existence'.

Many may think them mad. If they are revived hundreds, maybe thousands of years into the future they will start their new life old. Maybe they will benefit from age-prevention drugs, maybe they'll be able to undergo whole body transplants. Whatever the physical solutions, one problem would be incurable − the mental trauma of future shock. Waking up to a completely alien world, including in all probability new languages, social structures, foods, etc., might be enough for many of these experimenters to simply want to climb back into their nitrogen baths.

Gerontology is about preservation, but not in this way. The idea of the Methuselah Formula is to stay young and live through the ages amassing experience on the way. As we have seen in this chapter, knowledge and ritual have been passed down from generation to generation; ideas have been plucked from all areas of science, conventional or not, and are constantly being synthesised to find new ways of advancing. Now, it is no longer a dream that such knowledge could stay and grow within one generation – a generation that could live for hundreds of years.

CHAPTER SIX

The Methuselah Gene

All the functions that take place in our bodies do so on a cellular level. Whether it is the aging process, genetic illnesses or our well-being health-wise – everything is dependent on our cells. So what are our cells themselves, dependent on? Each of our body cells is itself a highly organised and complex business, in which the DNA is stored in the cell nucleus as the production manager. From here the various commands are given to the RNA couriers, the heads of department. After that the protein synthesis takes place in the production centres with the help of ribosomes. It is a production plant, in which raw materials are processed by enzymes, waste is sorted out and cleared away – a highly complex enterprise in extremely good working order. If however the production manager gives incorrect or misleading instructions because of faulty plans, mistakes occur in the production centres, which naturally affect the whole organism.

Human beings are so complex, it seems inconceivable that something so minuscule, a fragment of matter so tiny it is only visible under a high powered electron microscope, is responsible for what we turn into physically. DNA contains a wealth of information – a code that dictates exactly what we are. In effect, it is the program of life.

Every body cell has a nucleus, and every nucleus stores DNA molecules. These molecules are long, spiral-shaped, twisted, double cords, tangled together in 23 pairs of chromosomes. Unique messages, which control the chemical processes in every cell, are coded in a particular order of separate constituents called nucleotides. Apart from the flood of information for a complex organism equipped with living tissue, organs and systems, a nucleus also holds additional instructions for innumerable individual adaptions and refinements of the familiar basic concept. We are all human, but we are all different. DNA provides the billions of physical and mental characteristics that make every one of us a unique and unrepeatable creation.

Everything is registered in this information store: from the very tips of our hair down to our toe nails, from the growth of our teeth to our digestive tract, the colour of our eyes, the size of our ears – the list is endless. It is a mechanism of near infinite complexity which can only be explained if we start to think in molecules.

In 1953 the American J. Watson and his two English colleagues F. Crick and M. Wilkins worked out the physical structure of DNA, naming it, famously, the double helix. The scientists received the Nobel Prize in 1962 for their pioneering research.

The decisive concept of considering DNA as a kind of 'spiral staircase' came to Watson as he was having dinner at a Soho restaurant in London.

'I sketched the first outline on the corner of my newspaper during the return trip to Cambridge in a cold train compartment,' he said later.

The next day he discussed his idea with his colleagues Crick and Wilkins. As a result both researchers got straight to work, and only a few weeks later they managed to prove, by means of x-ray crystallographic photographs, that Watson's speculation was correct.

By hand, they had laboriously managed to build a model, which for the first time showed the structure of DNA, which in its basic form was similar to a twisted rope ladder. The bars alternately made up of phosphate and sugar molecules twist around each other in the form of a spiral. The rungs of this genetical rope ladder are connected by two of the sugar molecules, which are opposite each other. They are made up of the four nucleotide bases adenine, cytosine, guanine and thymine. All the hereditary information of an organism is determined in a genetic building plan by these nucleotides, which are anchored to the DNA cord in a specific order.

The initial discovery had taken years of painstaking research, but breakthroughs after it came thick and fast. In 1965, the American Robert W. Holley became the first person to decipher a genetic code. In 1967, the complete DNA cord of the virus 'Phi X 174' was synthesized by the American biochemist A. Kornberg.

And in 1970, the Indian Har Gabind Khorana reproduced a yeast cell gene in a test tube using several separate parts.

A little later on came a major achievement. In a joint effort the Americans H. Temsin and T. Baltimore and the Japanese S. Mizutani came across an enzyme in the human body, which proved to be invaluable to genetics. This enzyme makes it possible to reconstruct the DNA hereditary matter directly from the cells' own messenger substances. This considerably simplifies the deciphering of genetic codes. With restriction enzymes, for the discovery of which the molecular biologists Arber, Nathans and Smith received the Nobel Prize, geneticists have since then been able to dismantle the DNA cord of hereditary information and fit sections of genes back together in different formations. The genotype has therefore become a construction kit.

The biological clock theory of cellular genetic research is based on the findings of the American biologist Leonard Hayflick from the University of California in San Francisco. Like many other gifted scientists, Hayflick achieved his place in the hall of fame by questioning the foundation of a scientific dogma. This dogma had been established by the French physiologist and Nobel Prize winner Alexis Carrel – a quite enigmatic personality, who surrounded himself and his research in an aura of mysticism and eccentricity. (For instance, he insisted his assistants carry out their experiments in black robes and hoods.) According to his theory, human cells – all human cells – were immortal. He declared, 'If nothing gets in their way, they will divide and reproduce for all eternity.' Carrel began his experiments with the cells of young chicks in a nutritive solution. Thirty years later he presented these same cells, still alive, and declared them immortal. Carrel, however, did not know that he had been misled by inadequate technical equipment. His nutritive solution prepared from crushed chicken embryos had to be centrifuged off. But due to a malfunction of the centrifuge fresh embryo cells constantly got into the nutritive solution and therefore revitalised the cell cultures.

When Hayflick, working at the Wistar Institute in Philadelphia, began to doubt the correctness of Carrel's results he decided to settle the matter once and for all. In his laboratory, he placed cultures of human cells in a nutrient solution and watched carefully as these began to divide. As the cells neared the fiftieth division, he observed that the division process started to slow down. At the same time the cells began to suffocate on a non-soluble cell waste known as lipofuscin – brown fatty age pigments. In other words, the cells had aged. But they didn't just get older, after the fiftieth division they stopped reproducing altogether. There was no cellular immortality in normal tissue

Still not satisfied with this proof, Hayflick continued his project seeking more definite results. He established that the process of cell division could be interrupted – for example by freezing – and could be reactivated again later. For example, if the process of cell division was stopped after twenty divisions, it would continue for about another thirty times after defrosting; after that the cells aged and stopped dividing in line with expectations. Hayflick concluded that the cells were controlled by an inner clock, which was set precisely for a certain rate of division. These experiments became known as 'aging under glass'.

The Reality

Hayflick was convinced that the observations he had made in the laboratory were not only applicable to the corresponding process in the human body but to all aging processes. But what regulated the aging process of the cell? Where was the control centre, the clock?

Together with his colleagues, Woodring Wright from Stanford University and David Prescott from the University of Colorado, Hayflick developed a technique which allowed scientists to take the nuclei from several cells and transplant these into other cells. When the nuclei of old cells – cells, which for example had already divided forty times – were transplanted into much younger cells, these hybrid cells divided about another ten times and then stopped, in spite of the fact that the original cells had a life expectancy of forty further divisions. The exciting results occurred when the procedure was reversed. When young nuclei were transplanted into old cells, the old cells gained a new lease of life, dividing as often as the young cells. This clearly demonstrated that the controller of the cellular aging process was located in the cell nucleus. From his research Hayflick established that an hereditary command, exactly defined over the generations, becomes clearly recognizable. Cell cultures could otherwise by no means suddenly die off after an exact period of time when there is no change in the breeding conditions.'

'The conclusions drawn from these experiments are quite dramatic. A cell's loss of function, especially its ability to divide, is a programmed process imposed on various species and their tissue. We age, because to express it in computer language – the exact programme of our normal cells finally comes to an end'.

This phenomenon became known as the 'Hayflick

Effect'. Today, it is explained in a completely different way. For example, Dr. Robin Holliday from the National Institute for Medical Research in London believes that the death of cells is based on faults. He assumes that the proteins in young cells are normal and healthy, but the changes wrought by increasing age bring about a malfunction. The proteins become more and more fragile and, like the rotten beams of an old building, eventually collapse. Are such faults due to a genetic command? There is every reason to believe so. Dr. Holliday carried out a long series of experiments with fungi. It turned out that these so-called ever-lasting fungal growths began to age very quickly, as soon as faults crept in. Fungi, where no faults were smuggled in, continued to live on undisturbed. After extensive testing, Dr. Holliday and his colleagues conclude that it is these faults which trigger the process of aging.

Molecular biologist, Dr. Leslie J. Orgel from the Salk Institute in San Diego is also of the opinion that the aging process is closely connected to faulty proteins. He believes they are created during the synthesis of important molecules. 'Protein synthesis is a compli-cated process, as it is also carried out by proteins,' he explains. Theoretically, this means that as soon as faults have crept into the manufacturing process of proteins, the number of incorrect proteins will multiply rapidly. More and more faulty proteins are then developed from these incorrect proteins. Mathematically speaking, the reproduction of incorrect proteins takes on such propor-tions that it leads eventually to the cell not being able to function.'

Orgel, however, does not believe it is simply a case of a genetic disturbed plan within the cell nucleus. He ventures that incorrect proteins produce specific antibodies, which are linked to a kind of age aggression. The molecular biologist therefore sees cellular auto-immune processes as the fundamental cause of the acceleration of the aging process.

If the genetic command could be deleted, perfect proteins would be produced and man with his billions of cells would be, theoretically at least, immortal — provided, of course, that the problem really lies in 'programmed death'.

A number of scientists question whether aging and death — even if they are programmed in DNA — could be overcome in the foreseeable future. On the other hand one could object, that at the very least the effects of the genetic command could be combatted, even if there is no possibility of putting it out of action altogether. Any developments in this field would have to be an advance in the fight against old age.

The Russian biologist A. Olovnikov, from the Gamaleja Institute for Epidemiology and Microbiology at the Soviet Academy of Medical Sciences, offers a very convincing explanation for the Hayflick Effect. According to Olovnikov, DNA cords shorten with every cell division until finally the hereditary information is damaged. This damage is then inherited by the daughter cells, and so on in a process which has become known as 'marginotomy'. Olovnikov sees this as a plausible explanation for aging.

Sex and egg cells are however excluded from this decline of the genotype, because all hereditary information is required to guarantee succession. So marginotomy does not apply here. As all cells are derived from sexual cells, it must also be possible to activate the processes in the latter, thus assuring a passing on of perfect hereditary information.

Sex cells are created, divide and produce their DNA copies with the help of a special tandem enzyme called tandem polymerase. Normal cells have an inactive gene which prevents the functioning of tandem polymerase. If a way were discovered to activate this resting gene, there would be nothing more standing in the way of a prolongation of life. All hereditary information would remain intact, the Hayflick Effect would be avoided, and the death command in our life program would no longer exist.

So goes the theory. Unfortunately, the cause of the Hayflick Effect is not quite as clear as its preachers would like us to think. The 'fifty divisions and you're out' rule is by no means universal. Some give up sooner, like lymphocyte cells (immune system) dividing only twenty to thirty times. Some press on much longer. If the nutrient solution of cell cultures contained a cortisone or vitamin E supplement, the Hayflick limit was even exceeded by 100% and the cells of older animals transplanted into younger ones have been known to outlive the Hayflick limit threefold.

A few years ago the 'genetic clock' theory aroused considerable excitement within the scientific community after the presentation of sensational findings concerning cancer cells. Molecular biologists J. Carl Barrett and his colleagues from the research laboratory of Triangle Park in North Carolina had attempted to uncover what distinguishes normal cells, which age and die, from 'immortal' cancer cells. They fused a number of normal human cells with immortal cells from hamsters to make a chain of crossed cells. A large number of these hermaphrodite cells behaved like normal cells – they aged and finally stopped dividing.

Some however remained immortal. When Barrett and his colleagues examined these immortal cells more closely, they established that in all of them a certain chromosome, called 'human chromosome 1' was missing. When the scientists smuggled copies of this chromosome into the immortal cells, they became mortal again. They aged and ended the division process just like the majority of crossed cells. In this test the cellular aging process was apparently triggered by a gene in a *single* chromosome.

Fellow cell geneticists Vincent Christofalo and James Smith have been working on similar lines to prove that certain proteins are responsible for the switching on and off of cell division. Carl Barrett and his colleagues from the National Institute for Environmental Health Sciences in Triangle Park, North Carolina, also discovered that if human chromosome 1 was missing from the cell's genetic make-up it is indeed immortal.

It is a well known fact that the cells of all organs are equipped with a certain cell division program. For example, brain cells do not divide at all, whereas liver cells divide eighty times. In other words: the aging process of the cells, and the speed at which they divide and decline, varies considerably according to their function. It follows that the cooperation between the components of the organism will start off, like a group of countries setting up utopia, working perfectly together and with high ideals for the future. Unfortunately as the future approaches, arguments become more frequent – the liver refuses to take infected blood over its borders, the lungs decide they're only going to work at half capacity and the brain, overseeing the community starts to feel the effects – until one part gives out altogether and the whole system collapses.

Perhaps the Hayflick Effect is caused by defects slipping into the cell over time? Is the hereditary programme, DNA, partly or completely destroyed, and can the RNA message substances therefore no longer produce fault-free proteins due to loss of information? Does cellular mutation then occur, becoming a major factor that triggers the aging process?

As early as 1960, Ruth Hill, from the American Colombia University, discovered a group of enzymes, whose task it is to repair damaged DNA and to prevent mutation being passed on to the next generation of cells. This repair service which is only responsible for the DNA in the cell nucleus unfortunately does not work if the DNA of the mitochondria – the cell's power stations – is damaged. This is a promising area for further investigation.

The alternative to the damage theory would be genetically programmed death. This theory also includes the possibility that the lack of a genetic programme to preserve life could cause the aging process of mortal cells.

Gerontologists agree that hereditary dispositions play a decisive role in determining the length of life. This is not surprising as each of the sixty billion body cells of an individual regulates the complete biological functions of an organism with the help of about 100 000 different pieces of hereditary information.

In genetic testing American scientists have found out, for example, that sixty-two year old Helen Boley, a former employee of the US state department, is equipped with hereditary dispositions, which mean that she can expect a long life. In effect, she is the lucky recipient of the Methuselah gene.

As the tests showed, a very special juice flows in

Helen Boley's veins, for high life expectancy runs in her family. With the exception of her father, who died of cancer at the age of ninety, her maternal and paternal grandparents and great-grandparents reached an age of well over ninety, some over 100 years.

When the lab technicians at the University Clinic in Kansas tested the blood fat values of the lady, who was 5' tall and weighed 7 stone, they thought at first that their measuring instruments were playing tricks on them. For Helen Boley's values differed massively from the usual picture. It is known that there is 'good' cholesterol, HDL (High Density Lipoprotein), and 'bad' cholesterol, LDL (Low Density Lipoprotein).

At present an HDL value of 40 milligrams is normal, while a 150 milligramme LDL level is considered to be ideal. Helen Boley's HDL level was 200 milligrams and her LDL level was 80 milligrams per 100 cubic centimetres of blood plasma. In other words, Helen Boley's HDL was five times higher than the norm while her LDL was only half that of the average person. With these figures the risk of clotted arteries, strokes or heart attacks is almost zero. Tests proved that Helen Boley produced 'good' cholesterol three times quicker than the average person. According to the scientists, this is entirely due to genes. The lucky woman has obviously inherited this unlikely constitution from both her father's and her mother's side of the family.

Meanwhile scientists at the National Heart, Lung and Blood Institute in Bethesda are trying to track down the mysterious Methuselah gene, which promises a biblical age. They presume that the cooperation of two particular genes plays a decisive role. Firstly, the gene APO A1, which controls the production of HDL cholesterol. Helen Boley's is totally normal. Apparently her APO A1

11·56 11·57 11·58 11·59 12·00 12·01 12·02 12·03 12·04

Throughout evolution humankind has been imprisoned by time. Birth and death are the two certainties in life we cannot influence – or so received wisdom tells us – but all this is about to change in the forseeable future. Genetic researchers are already working on procedures which could bypass fate and control the processes of aging and death. *(Photo: The Image Bank)*

Top: A friendly round of cards in a retirement home. Old age can be a rewarding phase of life. As long as good care and suitable accommodation are provided, strong physical and mental health can follow.

Top right: The young hand symbolically nears the old. The 'contract of the generations' obliges the economically active to provide for the young as well as the old. The 'Methuselah formula' could render it largely superfluous.

Below left and right: Faces marked by the years. There is still no way to halt the decline. *(All photos: The Image Bank)*

With myths and religious illusions we try to make sense of death's mysteries.

Above: skulls at a Shinto burial ceremony.

Below: A cross on a Christian grave. Genetic technology will not be able to overcome death, but it will offer us a longer life expectancy. *(Photos: The Image Bank)*

The dream of immortality is as old as humanity itself, and the earliest known written artefact deals with the theme. This illustrated tablet from the Epic of Gilgamesh tells of the hero's meeting with Utnapishtim, who survived the flood, and to whom the gods revealed the secret of eternal life. The work dates from the end of the second millenium BC and forms the basis of Babylonian literature. *(Photo: Author's archive)*

Above: In the Amun temple in Kamak *(photo:Author's archive)* Alexander the Great searched desperately for the secret of eternal life, after an oracle had prophesised his early death. *(Portrait on a silver drachma, photo: Brian McCarthy, British Museum)*

Above: The pyramids at Giza. The ancient Egyptians believed the preservation of the body by mummification and costly tomb constructions ensured a pleasant life in the next world. The relief *(below)* shows the gods Toth and Horus sprinkling the Pharoah with the water of eternal life. *(Photos: Author's archive)*

One of the most puzzling characters in European history is the Count of Saint Germain. Man of the world, diplomat and universal scholar, he appeared in different places in Europe over a period of many decades and was always depicted as a youthful-looking middle-aged man. The mystery behind his unusually long life is as unresolved as the circumstances of his death. He always liked to stay at Louisenlund Castle in Germany *(above)* with his friend and patron Carl von Hesse-Kassel, who had an alchemy lab installed in a secluded tower to aid the Count in his research. *(Photos: Author's archive)*

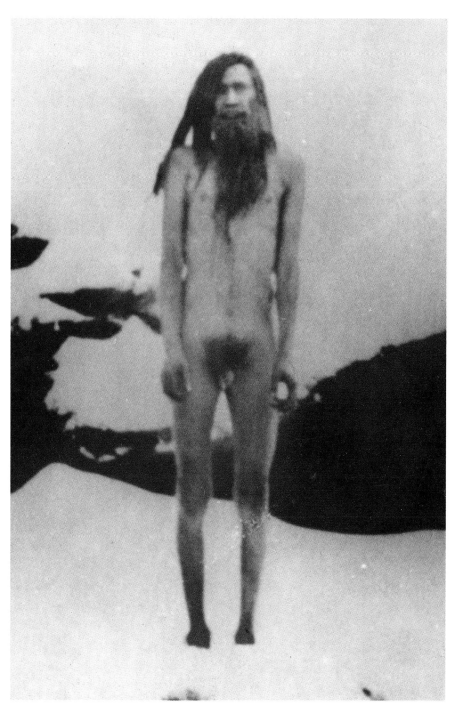

Swami Saresvarananda, pictured here in front of his snow hermitage, has lived in the Himalayas naked and without physical comforts for as long as people can remember. According to local folklore he is said to be over 650 years old. *(Photo: Author's archive)*

Left: Sri Ram Sharma Acarya Maharaj, a pupil of Swami Saresvaranand is over 87 years old and the picture of health

Below: The staff of Asclepius is the insignia of the Greek god medicine. Asclepius has been the symbol of medical skill since antiquity *(Photos: Author archive)*

Opposite: Today doctors have a vast wealth of medicines at their disposal, but an effective formula to extend life has not yet been discovered. *(Photo: The Image Bank)*

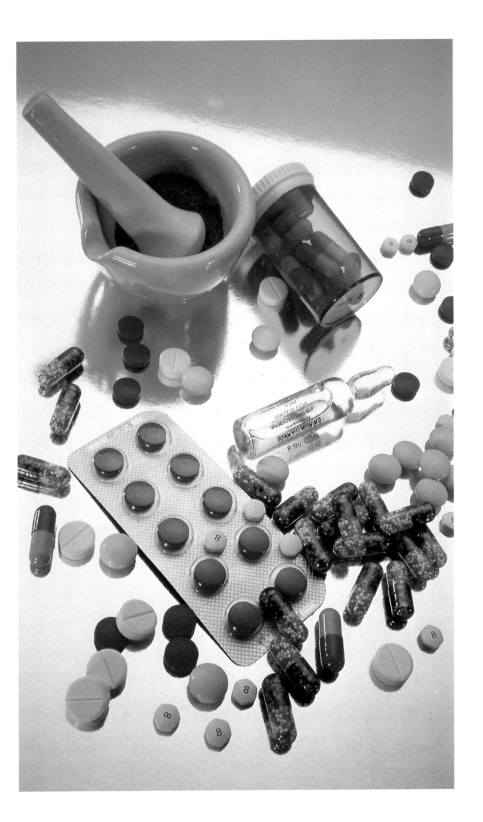

More effective preparations to extend average life expectancy are being sought worldwide in the laboratories of the pharmaceutical industry. *(Photo: The Image Bank)*

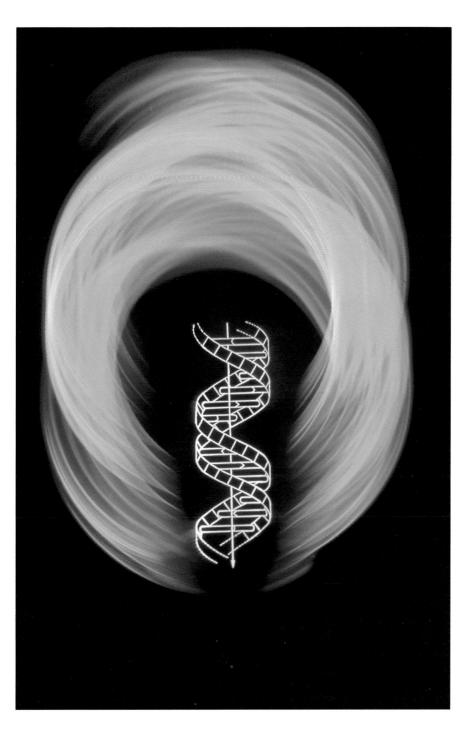

The DNA double helix – depicted here in a stylised model – holds the complete genetic code of life. Many scientists suspect that it holds a code that limits the amount of cell division and therefore the longevity of an organism. *(Photo: The Image Bank)*

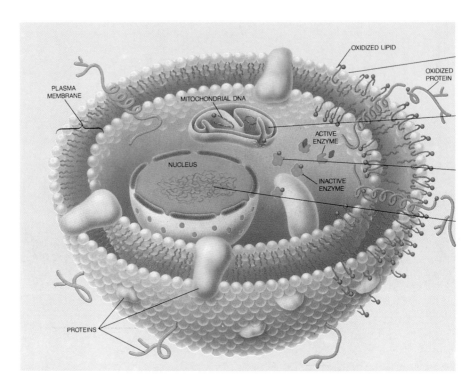

Above: Free radicals (blue) attack a body cell. They oxidise proteins (green), lipids (pink) and DNA (violet). They are therefore able to decisively impair cell functions. The formation of cancer cells can be triggered by free radicals. An accepted theory about the process of aging assumes that an organism produces more and more free radicals in the course of its life, until one day it becomes victim of their damaging effects.

Free radicals oxidise proteins and lipids on the cell membrane and thus kill the cell. The mitochondria are a preferred target of free radicals (2). If they are destroyed then the energy balance of the cell collapses. Free radicals can also de-activate effective enzymes inside the cell (3) and attack DNA found in the nucleus of the cell by impairing chromosome formation (4).

(From Scientific American, December 1992. Printed with the kind permission of the publishing house Spektrum der Wissenschaft)

Opposite page: The threadworm has been a common subject of genetic experimentation and research due to its relatively simple biological structure. *(Photo: Ken Abbott, University of Colorado)*

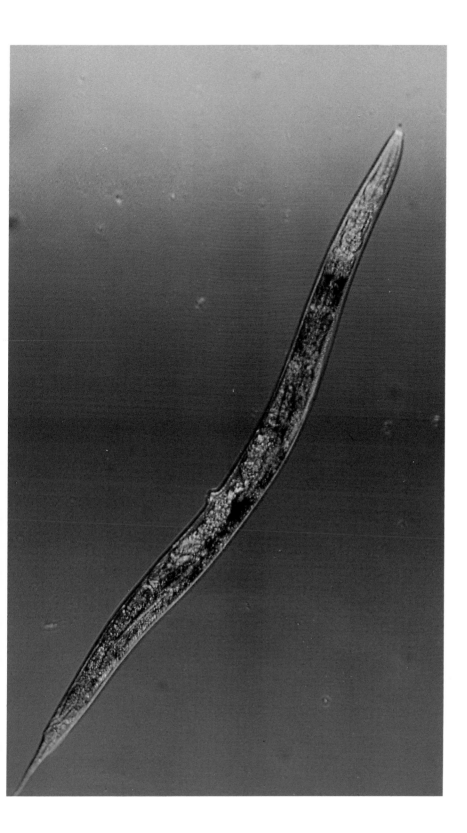

Biochemist Thomas Johnson, pictured here with an assistant, managed to extend the life of threadworms by genetic manipulation. *(Photo: Ken Abbott, University of Colorado)*

gene is influenced by the Methuselah gene which runs in the family. Blood from her mother as well as from close relatives is presently being tested to solve this mystery. According to Dr. William Harris from the University Clinic in Kansas there is certainly a connection between an extremely high level of HDL and a predisposition to longevity. The Bethesda scientist Dr. Daniel Rader is also trying to identify the mysterious gene, which could prolong the life of many people. If transplanted into other people, it would give us the ammunition to stave off blood clots and heart disease/ attack – some of the biggest killers known to the human race

Two kinds of animals have proved to be particularly suitable for genetic engineering tests: Fruit flies and threadworms. The geneticist Thomas E. Johnson from the University of Colorado in Boulder is experimenting with the threadworm Caenorhabditis elegans. He managed to isolate and change a gene in this threadworm. Normally this microscopic lifeform, the size of a comma, has a life expectancy of three weeks. By means of genetic manipulation in the genotype Johnson increased its life expectancy by 110%. The gene AGE-1 allowed the nematode to live for over one and a half months. Johnson is now convinced that there must be one or more genes in the human genetic programme, which correspond to the AGE-1 gene in the threadworm. Should these genes, which Johnson calls 'Geronto', really exist then it would be possible to use them to influence the aging process at its most fundamental level. 'If these genes could be isolated and then manipulated . . . methods of treatment could be developed which would significantly slow down the process of aging. We will prolong the life span of man in dimensions, which will go far beyond our previous imagination,' claims Johnson.

The thirty-nine year old American gerontologist and geneticist Michael Rose, professor at the University of California in Santa Cruz, even assumes a future life expectancy for humans of up to four hundred years. His optimism is based on the discovery of a life prolonging biomolecule. Together with his colleagues, Rose managed to breed laboratory fruit flies which lived for twice as long as is normal for members of this species. In one single biomolecule the scientists came across an elongation factor – EF1a. The geneticists had known for some time that fruit flies produce less and less body proteins with increasing age. Inspired by the results of the American geneticists, Professor Walter Gehring from the biological centre at the University of Basel assumed that an increased elongation factor in fruit flies could possibly activate and thereby increase their protein production. If aging and death of these insects was to be put down to poor protein synthesis, then it must be possible to extend their lifespan by generating more protein production. To increase the elongation factor Gehring smuggled a further gene into the heredi- tary substance of several fruit flies and simultaneously made sure their body temperature increased. The result was clear. The doubled dose of EF 1a considerably improved the life expectancy of the insects.

This is the first completely successful attempt of slowing down an aging process caused only by lack of protein. Researchers in this exciting area of gerontology believe it is major step forward, but it s just the begin- ning. 'We will extend life, no one can stop us now,' the American gerontologist and geneticist Michael Rose assures us.

The Methuselah Gene

In Germany, molecular geneticist Professor Karl Esser from the Ruhr University came across a life prolonging gene in the cell nuclei of mould *(Podospora anserina)*. Instead of twenty-five days, usual for this species, the mould lived for sixty days. Esser's research team then crossed several specimens of this type of mould, until finally a mould was created, which was equipped with two of these amazing genes. To all appearances this mould is completely immortal. Esser, who was awarded the Sandoz Prize by the International Gerontologistic Society for this research, said of it: 'Two of these moulds have now been living for eighteen years. It cannot be ruled out that man also carries such life prolonging genes.'

Surprisingly, when it comes to the number of years lost through early death, faults in the genotype are more costly than cancer, heart disease, diabetes and many other major illnesses. Thankfully, with the help of genetic therapy, many life-impairing genetic defects can now be eliminated. The damaged genes which lead to a number of illnesses have already been identified. Healthy genes are inserted into cells to take over the function of weakened genes. There are a number of approaches available to genetic engineers:

- medicines produced directly from genetic engineering;

- human genes, which can be combined with the hereditary substance of other organisms;

- using intestinal bacteria and dairy cows in genetic engineering as production plants for medicines, in which human proteins, enzymes or hormones can be manufactured as required.

Faulty genes can be discovered with genetic probes and a number of illnesses can be diagnosed more easily and more exactly with their help. In addition not only organs, but also genes themselves can be transplanted. The transplanted genes are able to repair faulty host cells when manipulated in the genotype of the body cells of an ill person.

There many different techniques for manipulating genes in human cells: with a fine pipette, by means of tungsten or gold shots, by electric shock or as a stowaway transported by a virus. Intervening in the genetic control centre allows us to regulate, divert or even activate and deactivate the processes of life with absolute precision. If the genetic manipulators can actually put their ambitious plans and ideas into practise, and they're already well under way, soon all kinds of life will be at their disposal, from the micro organisms of plants and animals to those of humans.

As soon as the central computer program of the DNA in the mini-protein production plant cells is completely deciphered, we will have broached the greatest scientific barrier in the history of mankind. The bio-genetic prospects are not only breathtakingly tremendous, but also breathtakingly awesome. The prospect of a cloned human has not without reason triggered heated debates, religious and philosophical, as to whether humanity should be allowed to do everything which is technically within their grasp. For whether we want to believe it or not a group of researchers at the George Washington University under guidance of Jerry Hall has actually had the courage to clone human embryos to twins and triplets. From seventeen embryos the scientists fathered a total of forty-eight brothers and sisters in a test tube – each of which was an identical copy of the other. Whilst such practices are undertaken with the closest of scrutiny and adherence to very strict laws, the fundamental question of whether we should be following this path at all has yet to be, and probably never will be, resolved.

German psychotherapist Dr. Rdiger Dahlke is pessimistic: 'The horror scenarios from Frankenstein or Dr. Mabuse have only a little left to offer mankind on the threshold of the third millennium. Our immediate reality is much more shocking. The news from the world of science is very serious. When we consider that in the USA, now the last superpower, the decision between ethics and money has for a long time favoured the latter, then a dreadful overall picture becomes apparent, a picture which overshadows many of the positive achievements we've been hearing about.'

Humans have already been subject to genetic alteration. In September 1990, the father of genetic therapy, the American W. French Anderson from the National Institute of Health made history by giving a four year old girl the first genetic treatment. The girl was suffering from an extremely rare and deadly adenosine deaminase (ADA) deficiency – a genetic immunity weakness. With the help of a virus Anderson slipped the corrected gene into the genotype of the white blood corpuscles. The genetic therapy was successful.

Perhaps the most ambitious plan is the three billion dollar genoma project to decipher the complete human genotype. This will open up a Pandora's box of potential for our species. 'The way we work with biology will follow a totally new path. We will have at our disposal a complete genetic blueprint for the human race,' the Harvard scientist Dr. Walter Gilbert enthuses.

The concept of a life of eternal youth without any time barriers – with all the consequences which arise – is no longer a flight of fancy. In fact, gerontologist Michael Jazwinski, from the Louisiana State University Medical Center, has stuck his neck out with his prediction that some of our *contemporaries* will still be around to deal with the problems this planet faces in four or five hundred years time. This may sound a little far-fetched but he offers as evidence his own 'fountain of youth' of yeast cells, and the results give pause for thought. He has investigated certain genes in young cells, one of which he called LAG-1 – longevity assurance gene 1. By increasing the activity of this gene in older cells the scientist achieved a 35% increase in the life span of these cells. Jazwinski reports that in human cells he has meanwhile come across DNA sections in the genetic program which are similar to his yeast LAG-1. The scientist now intends to smuggle human DNA into yeast cells so as to establish whether these also have a life extension effect. He is extremely optimistic.

Genetic discoveries are cropping up thick and fast. American scientists have also come across a super gene called MHC, which belongs to a gene complex in the sixth chromosome. In all probability this gene is responsible for the abatement of the immune system as well as for various geriatric illnesses. Cholesterol level, which is also connected to geriatric illnesses, is controlled by the genes in the liver cells. In this connection, scientists became aware of a strange phenomenon in the sleepy village of Limone, on Lake Garda. Its inhabitants not only enjoy excellent health, they also live longer than people anywhere else in Italy. This is because they have a special protein in their blood, called 'A1 Milano' by the scientists, which ensures they neither suffer from a stroke, nor a heart attack, nor artery calcification. The reason was only discovered a short time ago by the medic Professor Cesare Sirtori, when the village inhabitant Valerio Dagnoli underwent blood tests. His blood contained almost no cholesterol. The protein in his veins works like a broom, sweeping away fat deposits, and leaving the passages clean. 'It is five times smaller and quicker than a normal protein molecule. It is as if a Ferrari shoots through the blood,' Sirtori enthuses. The wonder protein is soon to come onto the market in the form of a medicine to extend life. 'We can already manufacture it artificially,' Sirtori claims.

For their research into the causes and problems linked to cholesterol build-up, the American geneticists Joseph Goldstein and Michael Brown from the University of Texas received the Nobel Prize for Medicine. In certain liver cells they located receptor proteins which control the LDL level. Even if only one or two of the genes responsible for receptor proteins are damaged, the LDL level in the blood increases excessively. In addition, Goldstein and Brown were able to prove that genes are responsible for certain types of heart diseases.

Genetic research often works in tandem with hormonal research. In the fight against aging and death, this link-up is producing miraculous results. Dr Daniel Rudman, endocrinologist at the Medical College of Wisconsin, found an amazingly easy way of stopping the clock of life. He acted as a kind of Mephisto, who in a six month long experiment, managed to reverse some aging symptoms in a group of sixty-five to seventy year old experimentees. Rudman used a human growth hormone as well as an effective secretion from the pituitary gland. This secretion supports the healing of wounds, strengthens the immune system, helps in the construction of bones and muscles as well as the inner organs and takes care of fat decomposition. From the sixtieth year onwards, the human body usually begins to age visibly. However, Rudman assumed that a hormone responsible for youthful vitality must also be in a position to restore it. So he carried out an experiment with twenty-one elder gentlemen, divided into two groups, which proved to be groundbreaking. One group received a synthetically produced growth hormone, HGH, three times a week, in a dose similar to that produced in the body of a healthy young man. The control group received a placebo. Extraordinary results appeared very quickly: Some members of the control group suffered deterioration in their organs, muscles and bones even quicker than Rudman had anticipated. On the other hand, the muscle growth of the experimentees, who were supplied with the growth hormone, amounted to 10% in only six months, while the skin thickened by 9% and body fat decreased by 14%. Rudman claims that in this way the aging process was delayed by a full twenty years.

The American gerontologist Jerome Wodinsky from the Brandeis University in Massachusetts is occupying himself mainly with the hormone system of female octopuses. After many years of research he has discovered two glands behind their eye sockets, which produce what he terms a 'death hormone' shortly after spawning, which makes the animals age and die in a very short time. Wodinsky is now considering, whether in mammals, including humans, such an aging and death hormone also comes into operation.

The American biologist Dr. Denckla makes similar assumptions. He managed to isolate a substance from the pituitary gland of a cow, which clearly makes the hormonal balance of all other glands collapse. Denckla therefore assumes that it must be possible to isolate a similar death hormone from the human pituitary gland. The next task would then be to develop an antidote.

Gene transplantation has also come to the aid of humans with chronically blocked arteries. Sensational trials from a research team at the American University of Pennsylvania concern a thirty year old Canadian woman from Quebec who was suffering from an extremely high cholesterol level, which was hereditary. The consequences were deposits in the arteries, a heart attack at the age of sixteen and a bypass operation at the age of twenty-six. Two of her brothers had already died from this illness at a very early age.

The research team operated on the Canadian and removed 15% of her liver, in which they placed new cellular cultures containing copies of compatible healthy genes. Doctors fed around a billion of these manipulated cells back into the liver via the blood circulation, where they established themselves with the best of results. At present, the patient's cholesterol level has reduced by 20% and according to the patient herself she feels 'very good. I can finally go dancing and skiing'.

And in Australia, perhaps one of the most significant discoveries yet is being put through its paces at this moment. The life span of human lung cells has been increased fourfold with the help of a special peptide. If this were extrapolated to cover the complete human organism it would indicate a life expectancy of 250 to

280 years. In these sensational experiments the scientists from Sydney could also prove, that even old cells could be rejuvenated. It seems that here a genuine fountain of youth has indeed been discovered. The first tests with mice have already started.

The incredible advances in genetic science have provided the foundation for understanding how we live and why we die. There is still a long way to go but at the current rate of progress, mere optimism is turning to certainty. We are made up only of cells. If we can make our cells live longer, then we can live longer. If we can alter our biological clock, if we can bypass the death program in our DNA, if we can stop faulty hereditary information being passed on within our bodies and from generation to generation . . . A lot of ifs, but only a few decades ago such possibilities seemed ludicrous, pie in the sky. Well, now we are touching the sky, we're bringing it closer. It s only a matter of time. In innumerable high-tech laboratories, gerontologists, geneticists and biochemists have declared war on illness, aging and death.

And they intend to win.

CHAPTER SEVEN

The Nutrition Bomb

'You are what you eat.' A well-known maxim. What goes in does not all come out. And what stays in can have a dramatic effect on our well-being. This is not exactly news but it is worth reiterating for so many people around the world ignore it. Most people accept that if you eat healthy food, you're more likely to stay healthy and if you smoke thirty cigarettes a day, washing them down with five pints of beer of an evening and grab a kebab on the way home, then chances are your excesses will come back to haunt you – with interest. What a lot of people don't know is that certain types of food, and certain vitamins can play a decisive role in slowing down the aging process. Healthy eating not only prevents your life being cut short, it can actually extend it beyond its original potential.

Over millions of years our eating habits have evolved in line with our bodies, and vice versa. We and our systems have adapted to the times – from the diet of the first monkeys, who looked for their food in the trees of tropical forests, right up to our modern-day selves, who mainly eat animal products and intensively farmed vegetables. When the forerunner of the 'wise man', the Homo sapiens, stood up on their back legs to walk upright, the first radical change began. Humans could use their grasping hands to hold tools and weapons and so could go hunting with a chance of success. From then on meat became their principal food. Fats, meat and proteins have been part of the human diet for several millions of years, whereas starch and sugar, as a part of our basic diet, have only been consumed for about 10,000 years.

Life differs from non-life by its adaptability to environmental changes. Changes in the structural, functional and behavioural patterns of animals can therefore also effect their nervous and glandular systems as well as the enzymic activity of the cells.

Enzymes are especially active protein substances, which are produced from living cells. They are catalysts, which steer and accelerate chemical compositional and decompositional reactions. The living cell produces a host of different kinds of enzymes, each only influencing one specific, clearly outlined procedure. Enzymes activate the processes which give us life and energy.

As a species, we have our brains and nervous system to thank for providing us with a decisive advantage over most other animals during the course of our evolution. The performance of the brain is primarily dependent on the effective working of the glandular system and the enzymic activity of the cells. Hormones, which reach the blood-stream via the glandular system, regulate the bodily functions. And catalysts take care of the bio-chemical reactions, through which the brain formulates messages passing them to the extremities of the body through our nervous system.

Since the beginning of its existence, the human race has been exposed to and has adapted to many damaging influences. We have had to contend with heat and cold, with wetness and drought, with injuries and infections but, above all, we have repeatedly had to put up with changes in diet.

How has this adaptability affected our development over the past few million years? A species can have insufficient adaptability powers for two reasons: firstly, because the organism cannot reproduce quickly enough to counteract a stressful and disadvantageous change in its environment; or secondly, because it cannot cope with such a strain over a sustained period of time.

The Canadian professor Hans Selye from Montreal, pioneer and internationally recognised authority in the area of stress research, has made a considerable contri-bution to the better understanding of this problem. He defines stress as the struggle for adaptability to a damaging factor.

The development from an ape-like being to homo sapien is said to have been decisively influenced by the rich and varied diet in the distant past. Millions of years ago Asia, Europe and Africa were joined together and covered with endless rain forests. The anthropoids, a sub-order of the primates from which we are thought to have descended, lived among many types of apes in these tropical forests. Their diet consisted of what they could find: mainly fruits, roots, nuts, plant shoots and leaves, but also caterpillars, insects, birds and their eggs as well as small animals and fish, when they managed to catch them. They thrived in the lush, wild forests, lived mainly in the trees and made their way to safety at the top if predators appeared.

The dilemma began with changes in the climate. Long periods of hot weather dried out the land. Without considerable rainfall, the tropical forests could not sustain themselves and thinned out, to be replaced, gradually, by savannahs. Anthropoids and apes were crowded together in an increasingly dense area. In the few jungle areas that remained they hunted each other's food, which was becoming more and more sparse.

On the other hand the grassy plains spread across vast continents and herbivores like horses and game grew in number. The anthropoids and their cousins had no other choice than to adapt to the changed environment; that means, they either had to accept the meat and bone marrow of these animals as their food or starve, as they could not graze like the herbivores, because they didn't have the chewing jaw required and the digestive organs used to process cellulose. Many anthropoids didn't survive. Those that did have reproduced up to the present day remaining as tree-dwellers feeding mainly on plants. Only a very few of the anthropoid cousins climbed down from the trees to seek their salvation in the plains. These few were the forerunners of modern humans. They learnt to walk on two legs, to hunt and to live from meat. Their new life in the plains was intensely difficult. Since they were not skilled enough to bag large grazing animals, they had to make do with injured or dead ones or eke out their existence with what they found at the edge of the woods — small rodents, who had left their holes, or larva, insects, bird's eggs, honey and suchlike.

With time they learnt to hide in the long grass, lie in wait for pasturing animals, who had lost their way and attack them. Next they hunted in groups. Co-operation between individuals for their common good became an important tool. They might, for example, block the way of a gazelle, using combined strength to haul their prey to the ground and kill it. They learned to use stones as weapons. With each leap they became more and more creative with the use of their eyes, hands and brain. Over the course of millions of years they gradually developed into Homo sapiens and began to make themselves understood by way of a primitive language.

With the grassy plains continually expanding, the supply of food for the growing antelope, buffalo, horse and cow herds increased — and with it the supply of prey for early humans, who hunted more boldly and more cunningly with new weapons like loops, clubs and spears. About 600 000 years ago these hunters discovered the use of fire which ensured survival through the on-coming ice age.

The process of adaptation, which turned the tree dwelling vegetarian into a cave inhabitant consuming meat, bone marrow and fat, was extremely difficult. It claimed many victims and dragged on over an extremely long period of time. As palaeoarcheology has been able to prove, the apes did not change in this time. Chimpanzees today still have the same bone structure as their prehistoric forebears and still live mainly from vegetarian food. Their pre-human cousins, who wandered into the plains and became carnivores, have on the other hand changed considerably. A defining step in the development of the modern human was the formation of sharp canine teeth, essential for breaking up tough pieces of flesh. Of even greater importance was a major change in our metabolism which allowed the liver and other organs to convert animals fats and proteins into energy. But the most important thing of all for our hominid predecessors was the fact that these new metabolic processes enabled the use of chemical constituents — mainly unsaturated fatty acids from the meat of herbivores — which contributed to the development of a larger and more capable brain.

An army of enzymes is responsible for the complicated chemical reactions of our cells. They enable our body to carry on its work trouble-free. These enzymes were perfected over thousands of generations, who at the beginning lived mainly on vegetable foodstuffs and later mainly on meat.

English nutritionist Dr. Richard Mackarness has concluded from these facts that 'A trouble-free mutation process and natural selection depend on a constant supply of suitable foodstuffs and a relatively stable environment.'

For example, it could be proved that a forced change of diet — as a consequence of a limitation of their usual life roving in the woods, was as much a reason for the heavy decimation of the elephant population in African animal reserves as the activities of illegal ivory hunters. It is also possible that the chemical treatment of foodstuffs in an industrial society leads to similar negative changes. Maybe the self-destruction of humans through degenerative illnesses cannot be excluded.

After hundreds of thousands of years of progressive seizure and exploitation of the earth and its natural resources, a ravaging that is accelerating exponentially, it is now the eleventh hour for Homo sapiens. A radical change in environmental and nutritional policies is long overdue. For the civilizations of Europe and America, the main culprits, it has literally become a matter of life and death.

Since the end of the previous century, when the processes of 'refining' and for that read 'distorting' our basic foodstuffs, started to take place on a wide scale, western civilisation has been increasingly afflicted by new epidemic illnesses. Degenerative illnesses of the heart, circulation, nerves, arteries, as well as cancer have taken the place of infectious illnesses which decimated earlier generations. If we now, all of a sudden, replace the chemistry of our organism, which has been used to meat for so long, by a high dosage of refined starches, sugars and a large amount of new chemical contaminants, then we must reckon with a collapse of important cell processes. The dangers entailed in interfering with the enzyme activity of cells do not seem to be appreciated by most people.

Nutrition is first and foremost an evaluation process of food by the organism. Our nutritional condition can be judged by the state of our bodily constitution and the balance between food supply and organism consumption. Healthy eating therefore means nothing more than providing our bodies with all the vital substances needed to run our system efficiently. Food must therefore not contain any natural or artificial contaminants for the body.

In the course of a lifetime, a single person eats their way through a food mountain of about fifty tons and has in contrast an average weight of about 150 pounds. Only a small proportion of food consumed remains even in the most corpulent of bodies. The main share of the food, which is absorbed into our body through digestion, is excreted again sooner or later. And only very few foodstuffs pass through our body unchanged, as most are transformed by one of the many metabolic chemical reactions.

The breakdown of foodstuffs is a prerequisite for the energy we need to maintain even the most inactive life. In some respects the body could be compared to an oven. For by using oxygen, fuel is burned. This leads to the release of energy in the form of warmth or power for bodily activities. This burning process however takes place slowly and step-by-step, so that the fire doesn't burn out and the heat remains constant

Thousands of different kinds of huge protein molecules – enzymes – which are present in all body cells and responsible for metabolic regulation, make the highly complex chemical processes of the body possible. For the fire of life must stay alive in a hostile environment – our body consists of 75% water.

After digestion, nutrients (absorbed food fragments) make up the raw material of metabolism. They are transported in the blood to tissue cells, penetrate them and serve as fuel or building material. The economy of the organism would however be badly served if nutrients were indiscriminately burnt, so that for example no amino acids were available for the repair of hand muscles, because these had been completely used up by the arm muscles. There is therefore a strict control of which fuel is used for which application.

The first point of control is the liver, which filters amino acids and carbohydrates from the blood as soon as they leave the digestive tract and go into general blood circulation. The liver needs several of these nutrients itself, but its main task is to exactly control and regulate the food supply of the body.

If carbohydrates are absorbed, the liver retains what

it needs to maintain its own carbohydrate depot in the form of glycogen (liver starch). As soon as the carbohydrates in the blood are used up, these are then released again. The liver filters amino acids from the blood, to manufacture plasma proteins, which are then reintroduced to the blood, as it has no protein store of its own.

The amino acid content of an organism is controlled by various hormones, especially growth hormones and insulin, which also regulate the use of carbohydrates. This hormone level in the blood has itself to control the number of animo acids which can be taken from the blood by, for example, muscle tissue. As soon as amino acids penetrate into a cell, that cell uses the quantity required for growth or repair work and burns the rest – and it deals with fats and carbohydrates in a similar manner.

One of our most essential requirements is, of course, water. Daily, we drink a good two litres of liquid in food and drink. Although one or the other can be subject to considerable fluctuations, this does not change the fact that about half of our food consists of water. The rest consists of a mixture of carbohydrates, fats and proteins. In the western world meals are, on average, made up of about 300 g of carbohydrates, about 150 g of fat and 125 to 150 g of protein.

The energy which powers our organism comes essentially from carbohydrates, fats and proteins. It is measured in kilocalories or kilojoules. Around 30 g of fat corresponds to 250 kilocalories, while the same amount of most carbohydrates corresponds to about 110 kilocalories. One exception among carbohydrates is alcohol, to be precise ethanol, 30 g of which makes around 200 kilocalories. Luckily, it cannot be taken undiluted and even high-proof spirits contain only one-third alcohol at the most – 64 kilocalories per 30 g. The remaining carbohydrates and protein, which are just as important for the bodily structure, supply the same number of calories.

Our food contains two main kinds of carbohydrate. The sweet tasting ones are generally the sugars, the bland ones the starches. One of the most simple kinds of sugar is glucose. This is the carbohydrate that's really needed by the cells in our body. Normally we understand sugar to be sucrose, a combination of a single glucose molecule and another single carbohydrate called fructose. Starches are also made up of glucose units in long chains of linked molecules. During the digestion process the compound carbohydrates are split into glucose and fructose according to their composition.

Proteins also consist of chains of single 'ingredients', amino acids. There are twenty amino-acids found in protein. The body produces thousands of different proteins, each made up of various amino acids ordered in various ways. The right mixture is necessary for the body to produce proteins. Of the twenty amino acids found in protein, there are eight which cannot be produced inside the body. These eight are therefore a critical factor in our nutrition. If only one of these amino acids is missing, protein synthesis is prevented and the remaining amino acids therefore become useless.

Fats are made up of glycerin molecules combined with three fatty acid molecules. The popular distinction between oils and fats is chemically unimportant. For oils are fats, which only have the characteristic of being in liquid form at room temperature. The temperatures necessary to melt fats are only determined by the fatty acids contained in them. Unsaturated fatty acids melt at very low temperatures, and oils, which contain such unsaturated fatty acids, are almost always liquid. They can be found in many vegetables, animals tissue and dairy products.

Cholesterol is one of the combinations of animal fats. The body can produce enough itself. But every excess in food is firstly absorbed and must then be excreted again. Egg yolk, butter, cream and fatty meat are particularly high in cholesterol. Although cholesterol is a necessary component of bodily tissue, excessive quantities of animal fat lead to an excess of cholesterol and so to heart disease and artery calcification.

So, food is a complex fuel combusted in our body to produce energy to keep us warm and to keep us active. As soon as we eat more than we need for this, the body stores superfluous energy in the form of triglycerides. In the body of vertebrates these substances form depot fat. There is only one way to become overweight: eat too much. There only two ways to lose weight: either eat less or use more energy. Reducing fat consumption alone, does not lead to an effective diet, as the body can also change carbohydrates and proteins into fat.

It is often claimed that carbohydrates make you fat, whereas protein keeps you slim, even though the number of calories in both is the same. The theory seems to have something going for it. While we can eat quite a lot of carbohydrate, especially in combination with sugar, food only containing protein and fat causes us to feel full and satiated. But it does not alter the simple fact that food we do not have cannot cause us to put on weight.

The number of calories required by an individual is

influenced by many factors and varies considerably from person to person. Some people lose weight with great difficulty even though they eat very little. For others, it doesn't matter what goes into their mouths; they stay slim. Manual work can cause an enormous consumption of energy. On the other hand intellectual work alone requires less energy. Larger people use up more calories than smaller people and women less than men when doing the same bodily activities. Children, pregnant women and women breast-feeding have also burn up more calories than the average person.

The amount of energy the body needs, the calorie consumption necessary for everyday living, is determined by our metabolism, the rate of which is measured by the basal metabolic rate – the metabolic speed of a person at rest.

This rate fluctuates throughout our life. New-born babies have a very low rate, but it rapidly reaches a peak in the second year. After that it slowly decreases until puberty and then it remains constant, until full maturity. In middle age and old age it slowly decreases again. These are general trends: our metabolic rate can change from month to month depending on what we do and what we eat. The metabolic rate of permanently hungry people decreases by up to 40% to compensate for a perceived, or real, lack of food. (In effect this means that dieting, as opposed to permanently changing your food habits, can actually make you put on weight. If you suddenly eat drastically less, the metabolic rate drops to compensate. When you give up your diet, you go back to your normal eating patterns but your body is only burning up as many calories as it was previously, resulting in an excess intake of energy and, consequently, weight gain.)

Growing children have the highest protein requirement as it is essential for growth. Adults, on the other hand, only need it to maintain their bodily tissue; about 30 g daily is sufficient. Getting your daily requirement is no problem as most foodstuffs are extremely rich in protein. Bread, for example, gives almost the same amount as beef, milk or watercress.

In 1979, at a Hamburg conference under the motto 'Loss of performance due to a lack of nutrients', Professor Ludwig Prokop, in his capacity as Director of the Austrian Institute of Sports Medicine, stated: 'The idea that the public receives good nutrition due to the surplus of various foodstuffs in our affluent society, has unfortunately proved to be a great misjudgment. Our diet is unbalanced and we have lost our natural instinct for eating the right food. Coupled with the irresponsible, subconscious programming of eating habits through advertising, the situation led to serious health problems in developed countries. It is obvious that performance in everyday life and at work is impaired by the wrong diet and this leads to mistakes, strain and genuine damage to health.

'The idea that performance and stamina are clearly reduced before clinical symptoms of deficiency appear must be taken on board as fundamental if we are to improve our well-being. There may be nothing wrong with us, but we certainly aren't maximising our potential. This is especially true when it comes to vitamins, minerals, trace elements and enzymes. When clear symptoms of malnutrition (as opposed to undernourishment) appear, the situation is often aggravated further by short-sighted and biologically unsound diets that are often little more than fads.

'After all it is also a question of how far it is possible

to achieve not only an improvement of general performance but also effective protection against outer and inner stress factors by enhancing food with vitamins or other biocatalysts.'

At the same conference, Dr. Klaus Pietrzik, Senior Assistant at the Institute for Nutritional Science at the University of Bonn, said:

'Investigations from many countries unanimously show that despite an oversupply of calories the desired level of vitamin supply is not always guaranteed . . . Statistical valuations in nutrition reports show that the intake of certain vitamins, especially in the case of children and young people, is up to 30% below the recommended daily intake.'

In this connection the investigation of meals in fourteen canteen kitchens in a West German city produced the following disturbing results: In hospitals, old peoples' homes, all-day schools and in the meals-on-wheels service, 8600 people (3.6% of the total population) were catered for. The nutritional guidelines concerning copper, magnesium, zinc and ascorbic acid were kept to. But the following problems were highlighted:

— The meals contained 52 % fat.

— The required protein content was 1.7 times too high.

— Phosphorus, sodium and cholesterol levels were much too high.

— The supply of linolic acid, vitamin A, vitamin E, potassium, calcium and iron were woefully insufficient.

— The maximum allowable value for cadmium was
   exhausted.

Scientists were particularly concerned about the
amount of salt in the canteen meals. For with the
midday meal alone the required daily amount had
already been exceeded by two and a half times, and
this didn't include the widespread habit of adding more
salt before eating.

These comments and surveys are, admittedly, fifteen
years old and dietary awareness is improving, but they
highlight deficiencies in our diet which still exist today.
We eat too much salt, too much fat and not enough
vitamins. The *majority* of people in Europe and the USA
fall into this category. For an indication of how
dramatic the effects of such diets and lifestyles can have
on your health, you only have to look at the results of
the following study:

Over a period of many years the habits and health of
two opposite groups were compared: those who
exposed themselves to various risk factors, smoked and
drank heavily, ate food at random and rejected vitamin
preparations, and those who had committed themselves
to healthy eating and regular taking of vitamin
preparations.

The results of the blood analysis clearly showed that
the regular supply of vitamins coupled with a healthy
diet to a clearly improved sense of well-being. Those
who lacked vitamins and trace elements often suffered
considerable problems, particularly when deficient in B
complex vitamins. The first group were more likely
to experience exhaustion, heart disturbance, skin
problems and nervous disorders.

Other tests have clearly established a link between

poor diet and the following:

- Depression, sadness, pessimism

- Insomnia or constant tiredness

- Nervous unrest

- Retardation, delayed development

- Weakness, loss of energy

- Loss of libido

- General apathy

- Feelings of guilt

- Lack of concentration

- Physical problems.

A good example of how unnatural our diet has become can be seen in the case of wheat flour. A staple in almost everyone's diet, it has been freed of just about every valuable nutrient in its refined form. But instead of consuming it as intended what we end up with are bleaching agents to guarantee a perfectly white loaf. One of the agents commonly used, chloroxide is a poison used to trigger diabetes in laboratory animals. Chlorine bleaching agents are used to remove the wheatgerm oil contained in the corn. Oil in flour is a problem for commercial bakers, as the flour then becomes sour more easily and attracts insects.

Even in unbleached flour, half of the oil is lost when the wheat is milled – very unfortunate, for wheatgerm oil contains only unsaturated fatty acids which have a high nutritional value. Vitamin E is also destroyed by the milling process. And so is a large part of the protein. The consumer, therefore, only receives very low quality proteins with normal wheat flour. In addition the following mineral losses occur: almost 50% of calcium; 70% of phosphorous; 80% of iron; 98% of magnesium; 75% of manganese, 50% of potassium and 65% of copper.

On the way from the wheat grain to white bread the vitamins are also almost all left behind:

Approximate Depletion	
Thiamine (vitamin B1)	80%
Riboflavin (vitamin B2)	60%
Niacin (vitamin B3)	75%
Pantothenic acid (active principle of the B vitamins)	50%
Pyridoxine (vitamin B6)	50%

These figures are the results of a study carried out by the College of Agriculture at the University of California. This list is by no means complete, but it makes it perfectly clear how damaging modern food processing techniques can be.

A unique mega-study published in the American *Journal of the National Cancer Institute* triggered a 'vitamin euphoria' among experts. American scientists had conducted an experiment with a huge 30 000 participants in the northern Chinese region of Linxian to determine the cause of a conspicuous increase in the number of cases of gastric and oesophagus cancer. The mortality rate for this condition was about one hundred times higher there than in the United States. The farmers there eked out their existence under pitiful circumstances and had to live on a very one-sided diet, consisting mainly of sweet potatoes. Fruit and vegetables were scarce and meat was a rich man's luxury.

Over a period of five years one section of the experimentees was given a daily vitamin cocktail, which well exceeded the recommended daily intake. The control group on the other hand was fed placebos.

The results caused a sensation. In those who received the vitamin cocktail the mortality rate dropped 9%, cancer related deaths dropped 13% and the gastric and oesophagus cancer rate fell by an amazing 21%. The antioxidant cocktail made up of carotene, selenium and vitamin E proved to be especially effective.

According to many experts this massive study supplied us with the first irrefutable proof that cancer could be prevented by specific vitamin doses. A large-scale Finnish study carried out on 29 000 smokers has since proved that specific doses of vitamin E and beta-carotene can help to protect against lung cancer.

The American biochemist and nutritionist, Professor Carlton Frederiks, describes the nutritional collapse of the organism due to an insufficient supply of vitamins, enzymes and trace elements as follows:

– Deficiency symptoms, caused by an unbalanced diet, develop step-by step.

– The sequence begins in the blood. If the supply of nutrients is reduced there, then the tissue reserves are called in. As soon as these are exhausted, the food is withdrawn from the organs. Malfunctions can already appear in this phase – vague or clear symptoms, which unfortunately are mostly not diagnosed as being caused by nutritional deficiencies. This is following by tissue changes at a cellular level. Subsequent tissue defects become apparent to the naked eye.

– It must be emphasised that visible changes in the tissue, such as bleeding of the gums or neuritis, occur before the emergence of alarming symptoms.

– Resistance to infections is reduced and general vitality suffers; increase in stress levels, behavioral disturbances and subtle, undesired changes in personality may also appear.

We could pay the price for this in premature aging – and if the deficiency leads to more fundamental failure of the functioning of the body, death is a possibility. The connection with nutritional deficiencies is often only recognised, when external signs become visible and the damage already done is difficult to repair.

This process is known as the 'nutrition bomb', a time bomb which is programmed early but explodes later on. Even people who think they are eating healthily may suffer from it because many of the trace elements and vitamins our body needs are difficult to find in today's over-refined diet.

Vitamins are extremely complex organic substances, consumed in minuscule doses, which help to keep the body fit. We normally know them under the letter they were given when they were discovered. Some, however, have special names, eg biotin and folic acid. Others are often to be found under their chemical terms like pyridoxine, pyridoxal and pyridoxamine, which mean nothing else than the term common to us all – vitamin B6.

Vitamins have the most varied effects. Some seem to support the enzyme activity of the organism, while the function of others has still not been fully explored. The following points, however, are established facts:

– Our health depends on the effects of the smallest amounts of vitamins present in the body.

– Vitamins are not direct suppliers of energy, but without them carbohydrates, proteins and fats can not be turned into energy.

– Food and vitamins are equally important.

– The organism dies without vitamins.

– The vitamin requirement of every individual depends on the ability of the organism to utilize them accordingly. There are considerable differences here.

– Although every vitamin has a specific task to fulfil in our nutrition, they all work together as a team. Certain vitamins won't work at all unless others are present.

– Even if the effect of a vitamin is impaired by the absence of another, no vitamin can replace another.

– All vitamins are required for the undisturbed functioning of the glands and for keeping the tissue intact.

— A healthy balance between destructive and constructive cellular processes can only be maintained by a combining of all vitamins. As soon as this balance is disturbed, decay begins – the cells degenerate or age prematurely.

— The more vitamins are missing in the organism, the quicker the symptoms of decay become noticeable.

— Vitamins noticeably affect the hormone production in the body.

— Vitamins support the tissue in warding off infections.

— Vitamins have the effect of a spark plug on the organism.

— An extreme lack of vitamins and poor nutrition lead to decay and death; a partial lack of vitamins leads to a loss of strength and illness. This stage of slowly losing strength is known as premature aging.

— Cells which are already dead cannot be reconstituted, but cells under attack can be normalised through treatment with vitamins.

Vitamins are sensitive. Some are destroyed by the oxygen in air, others by heat, water or inorganic iron in their surroundings. While, for example, Vitamin A is destroyed by the influence of oxygen, vitamin B1 and B2 are destroyed by long cooking. Boiling water washes the goodness out and light makes them ineffective. That is also the case with vitamin B6 and folic acid. Soaking in water and cooking damages vitamin C. This vitamin is ineffective in wilted fruit and vegetables. Vitamin E is spoilt when brought into contact with inorganic iron.

There are two groups of vitamins: water-soluble and fat-soluble. The B complex vitamins and vitamin C belong to the first group. Vitamins A, D, E, V and K belong to the latter. Fat-soluble vitamins can only be absorbed by the body if fat is included in the food. The body cannot store water-soluble vitamins, so they must be freshly supplied on a daily basis.

The experts are divided over the exact amount of additional vitamins, enzymes and minerals we should be prescribed. An excess of certain vitamins (D, for instance) can, in some cases be harmful. However, there is no doubt that they are, on the whole, actively beneficial. For decades the two-time Nobel Prize winner and 'vitamin pope' Linus Pauling took, in addition to his normal food, up to 50 g of vitamin C, 800 mg of vitamin E as well as the vitamin B complex, selenium and zinc daily. He lived happily to an age of almost 100 years.

Drs. McCay and Comfort have carried out animal experiments with different nutritional concepts. Dr. C. McCay from the Cornell University, one of the leading experts in the field of connections between aging and nutrition, is looking for the key to longer life through perfect diet. After twenty-five years of experiments with rats he has become convinced that nutritional deficiencies are responsible for all possible afflictions, whether blindness, general frailness, premature aging or, ultimately, death. He concludes that it must be possible to keep the organism young by giving it extra doses of vitamins and through this extend the life of the recipient. McCay worked with two groups of rats.

The Nutrition Bomb

While one group was allowed to eat as it liked, the other group received less calories, but a carefully balanced amount of proteins, minerals and vitamins. The aging process of this diet group was visibly delayed. After 1000 days – a period which corresponds to 100 human years – they were healthy, normal, active, had shiny fur and most breathtaking of all, they had yet to even reach full maturity. When McCay gave them normal food, they were fully grown in no time and reached double the age of control group of rats.

Comfort, gerontologist at the University of London, approached his subjects a little more drastically, under-feeding his test mice by making them go hungry for two days in every seven. This method had clearly beneficial results. The life of the mice was extended by 50%.

Clearly, there are ways to defuse the nutrition bomb, there are ways of making sure it never starts ticking in the first place – it's just a question of knowing your vitamins, minerals and trace elements, what each one does and where to find them. Medically, the jury is still out over which and how much, but there is a consensus that a balanced diet and extra vitamins will leave you feeling better and, potentially, living longer. For a detailed run down of my personal nutrient program and a comprehensive list which details natural food sources and which vitamins do what, refer to the appendices. In the meantime you could do worse than consult the next chapter which focusses on a particular vitamin of remarkable anti-aging powers.

CHAPTER EIGHT

Radicals *v.* the wonder of E

An essential component of almost all animal cells are lysosomes. One of their functions is to break down the nutrients absorbed into the cells. They also regularly break down parts of the cellular structure, which are then later renewed by protein synthesis.

In a way, lysosomes are a demolition colony, made up of a small microscopic sack with a wafer-thin membrane, housing a crew of potent digestive enzymes. These enzymes are dedicated to certain areas of decomposition. One lysosomal enzyme decomposes DNA. Another attacks the RNA which renews the cellular materials and structures. Other enzymes attack other molecules, including proteins, and destroy them. Lysosomal enzymes basically have the ability to break to break down all the essential components of life.

Because the membrane is so thin, it is easily damaged and the destructive enzymes often seep into the rest of the cell. It's in their nature to destroy and they run riot through what was once a healthy cell, ripping its basic structure apart. Over time, due to this process, cell function is damaged or stops completely

Scientists are convinced that in the course of life many, perhaps most, of the billions of cells that make up our body lose their ability to function either partially or totally. With the degeneration of the cells, organs and tissue perish until the whole organism gives up. For the enzymes leave the cells, flood the extracellular space and attack connective tissue, gluing it together with collagen. For some time now, these processes have been an area of intense research to discover just how damaging they can be to our bodies.

Membrane collapse is not an unusual phenomenon; it recurs in all forms of life. For example the male and female sexual hormones – testosterone and progesterone – are particularly ferocious, damaging cell and lysosomal membranes. Or the attack can come from outside influences: bacterial poisons in the course of an infectious disease; the sun's ultraviolet rays; from X-rays and radiation to name only a few.

One of the main causes of cell damage, however, is a chemical reaction known as lipide peroxidation which takes place regularly as part of every normal cell metabolism. Ironically, this involves the reaction of lipides (fat-like substances), from which cell membranes are made, with oxygen, on which everything in life depends.

In the course of this process a special type of reactive molecule comes into play – the dreaded Free Radical.

These can induce a mass of lysosomal enzymes to 'storm the Bastille' and in extreme cases can destroy the whole cell.

'Up to now we had assumptions, but no proof,' says Rajindar S. Sohal, one of the workers on the project at the University of Texas in Dallas. 'Now we're certain. The Free Radical Hypothesis is applicable to aging.'

According to this hypothesis, aging is mainly due to the destruction caused by Free Oxygen Radicals, which accumulate with time. We have seen how they are produced on a micro-level, but the overall picture is that these electrically loaded oxygen molecules are damaging by-products of the combustion processes in the body. Body cells use oxygen during combustion so as to produce energy for metabolism.

Free Radicals make holes in the cellular walls, destroy sections of the genetic material and can even trigger chain reactions.

'The destruction work done by the Free Radicals is the price that all living creatures have to pay for their life,' Sohal said. This is just as valid for the tiny fruit fly as it is for whales.

Researchers in Dallas are breeding fruit flies with the help of genetic manipulation, which produce far greater amounts of the enzyme peroxide dismutase than those found naturally. As both of these enzymes fight Free Radicals, they can reduce their dangerous side-effects. The results were encouraging. The genetically engineered fruit flies showed increased resistance to Free Radicals by about 50%, and their lifespan increased, on average, by 30%.

Due to the results of several research projects, it is now known that Free Radicals can trigger a whole host of illnesses and geriatric complaints. The basic problem is that they can be caused by so many factors over which we have little control. Air pollution, environmental poisons, pesticides, food preservatives, heat, sunlight, strenuous exercise, and even by breathing.

One of the pioneers of Free Radical research is doctor and chemist, Denham Harman, from the University of Nebraska. He has proved that oxidations triggered by Free Radicals cause similar biological damage to that of aging. This also causes increasing changes to collagen and elastin (protein substances of the elastic connective tissue), of the vascular walls, chromosomes, and last but not least the formation of the cellular waste, lipofuscin, which in the course of the aging process is deposited in certain cells. Lipofuscin is particularly important because when excess amounts of it are produced they take over large parts of the cell, rendering it largely ineffective

All cells renew themselves several times in the course of life, with two noteworthy exceptions – heart tissue and brain ganglia. Ganglia carry news messages around the human brain and spinal cord. If these cells were subjected to continued renewal, such a process would mean an interruption in the flow of news and a potential shutting down of the brain. The same applies to the heart. It beats from the first to the last second of our life. Cell renewal would make life difficult.

In the course of the aging process lipofuscin is deposited in the immortal cells of the ganglion and hinders the metabolism of the nerve cells. For a few years it has been known that several components in the brain cells do renew themselves. This also includes the grain-like mitochondria, the power stations of the cells. They take care of the energy metabolism in the cell through a number of enzymes. Even if several cellular components are exchanged, the age pigments always remain in the cell and influence the performance of the brain as it grows older.

There are a number of radical catchers or antioxidants to fight the Free Radicals, which combine with the radicals to defuse them. Some are in the human organism naturally, for example the enzyme peroxide dismutase, which combines with oxygen radicals, or the enzyme macroxyproteinase, which clears away the damaged amino acids and cellular waste.

At the University of Hohenheim, Professor Klaus Bayreuther is experimenting with the substance Centrophenoxine, which is gained from the plant growth hormones, auxin and acetylcholine. Centrophenoxine is supposed to clear the cells of the unwanted waste created by Free Radicals. Using this drug, Bayreuther has already managed to increase the life of his laboratory animals by 30-40%.

The substances stemming from vitamin A – Beta carotene, vitamin C, and E all belong to a vital group of agents known as antioxidants. These fight Free Radicals, preventing or curbing the destructive process of lipid peroxidation. They also delay the process of fats becoming rancid, which is based on the absorption of oxygen in the air by unsaturated fatty acids. This oxygen, without which we would suffocate, develops poisonous by-products in our body when reacting with fats in the liver. The same process which lets fat, butter or grease go rancid in our kitchen also takes place in our bodies.

Vitamin E is by far the most important member of this group and has become known as the wonder vitamin. Of all the natural anti-oxidants it is the strongest, leading the fight against the destruction of vital, sensitive substances by Free Radicals. Its particular effectiveness is down to a co-enzyme named Q 10 which is of the utmost importance in the process of transforming food into energy, as it acts as a catalyst for other enzymes in the body to do their work.

The biochemist John P. Richie, from the American University of Louisville, is presently testing the antioxidant NDGA (Nordihydroguaiaretic acid) and has doubled the life span of female mosquitos with it. This opens up interesting possibilities of fighting the problem of Free Radicals in humans.

Vitamin E, however, is not only an antioxidant. Its beneficial attributes are almost endless. Discovered in 1922, it soon became known as essential for reproduction and prevention of muscle wasting. According to reports from the nutritional experts Dr. Bicknell and Dr. Preskott the history of illness in children suffering from muscle wasting right from birth, led to the conclusion that their mothers had a vitamin E deficiency during pregnancy and the period of breastfeeding. By 1947, one of its main wonder properties had been established. Remarkably, it was an effective treatment for various kinds of heart complaint. Canadian Dr. Evan Shute was the first to use the vitamin in this way, treating his seventy-one year old mother who was suffering from angina pectoris and whose arms and legs showed oedemas. After only five days of taking the vitamin, the pains and the accumulation of water around the extremities disappeared.

As a result Dr. Shute and his brother Wilfred used vitamin E on other patients with heart disease and within three years they had tested it on 4000 patients. 80% showed amazing success; most of the patients left the course free of their serious heart complaints. Today vitamin E is prescribed all over the world to treat heart conditions and high blood pressure.

Meanwhile it has come to light that vitamin E, amongst other things, increases the life of the red blood corpuscles and positively influences the metabolism. It can prevent fat concentrating in the blood and so prevent calcification of the arteries. It has even been known to reverse existing arterial damage and improve blood circulation.

Vitamin E also has dramatic effects on the pituitary gland which plays a major role in keeping our levels of hormones balanced. For those suffering an imbalance, the pituitary gland can be stimulated by high doses of vitamin E until it normalises again. A deficiency of vitamin E, however, can cause serious disorders. In the most severe cases it can lead to damage of the connective tissue and liver, stillbirths, sterility and heart problems.

The amount of vitamin E in the body is higher than that of all other vitamins because it is a crucial agent in so many of the chemical processes that take place in our body. It's vital for the health of our muscles, it protects vitamin A, linoleic acid and probably other nutrients against oxidisation and, in the case of A, from rancid fats. Research also suggests it has important links to the working of the thyroid gland and the nervous system.

It is also used for thrombosis, liver and kidney conditions, chronically ulcerated legs, serious burns, gangrene in the early stages and has shown amazing promise in the fight against cancer. (During experiments with rats it was observed that cancerous tissue does not continue to grow if it is subjected to blood serum with added vitamin E. If this vitamin is missing in the nutritive liquid, then the cancer growth carries on undisturbed.)

It is really amazing what vitamin E can do . . .

— It is vasodilative, especially on the capillaries and can so stimulate the circulation of blood to poorly supplied muscular tissue.

— It lowers the oxygen requirement of muscular tissue by 50%, again increasing circulation.

— Tissues and nerves are strengthened.

— Pain and difficulty when breathing is reduced.

— As an antithrombin — a substance which stems clots — it dissolves blood clots or prevents their formation, without having a negative effect on the body's natural clotting ability.

— It prevents the formation of excessive cicatricial (scar) tissue and in some cases even recedes it.

— It stimulates urine excretion and is therefore particularly beneficial to heart patients with dropsy.

— It maintains and protects the blood vessel and capillary walls — essential for preventing heart defects.

— It increases the circulation of collateral connections — the links between the blood vessels — and supports the formation of new blood channels, i.e. the construction of diversions around blocked veins and arteries.

– It boosts muscular strength and performance, and consequently keeps the heart in good order.

– It supports the effectiveness of other vitamins.

Regrettably, most of our natural sources of vitamin E, in vegetable oils and wheat-based products like breakfast cereals, are lost through refining and hardening. This vitamin is also practically non-existent in fruit, butter, cream, yeast, dripping, cod-liver oil, white rice, refined maize or wheat flour. The modern steel roll milling procedure totally destroys the vitamin E in flour. This lack of a natural supply for such a vital nutritional component is without doubt one of the reasons for the considerable increase in degenerative illnesses, which has been identified since the introduction of the milling process about one hundred years ago. According to renowned nutritionists, the daily per capita supply of vitamin E before the introduction of steel roll mills was estimated at 100 to 150 mg. Today our food contains about a tenth of that at the very most.

As we have seen, a major part of the Methuselah Formula is based on recent scientific developments. But the gene biologists can't help us if we don't help ourselves. You can have a machine with the potential to run perfectly for hundreds and hundreds of years, but if you don't look after it, it will break down. Maintenance is as crucial as the design. In other words, what you put into your body is as important as what scientists can do with it. We all need the right vitamins and nutrients to survive. Vitamin E is particularly important, because it helps in so many of the millions of chemical reactions that keep our bodies working day in day out.

If you want to grasp eternal youth by the hand, if you want to be ready to reap the benefits of these amazing scientific developments you'd better be careful what you eat and what you do. After all, a formula is usually the product of many parts and many approaches. Methuselah is no different.

The Future

CHAPTER NINE

Laugh Yourself Young

If you are happy and laugh a lot, you can extend your life. At least that's what some American scientists have established. They have proved in a series of tests that the mind has the power to control the immune system. That means that a positive attitude to life and a tendency to see the bright side of difficult situations make your system stronger when it comes to the task of seeing off viral and bacterial attacks.

It seems too simple to be true. Laugh in the face of illness and it disappears. Pull the other one. Believe it or not the evidence is there. For example, a group of students were shown films of sketches by comedians which made them burst out laughing. When their blood was tested afterwards it was found that the amount of white blood corpuscles in their blood – the body's health police – had rapidly increased.

When Dr. William Fry heard of the results of these experiments, he decided to submit the patients in his clinic in San Francisco to similar experiments. He arranged for them to be repeatedly exposed to humorous situations. The result: reaching for painkilling medicines decreased considerably. Unfortunately, it could not be proved whether the patients were distracted from their pain by their happiness or whether their laughing released the body's own opiates – tests weren't carried out.

Other doctors, however, adopted a more scientific approach that stands up to closer scrutiny. They hypnotised their patients and made them visualize their white blood corpuscles as voracious sharks swimming through their blood, seeking out viruses and bacteria and devouring them. The consequent blood tests showed that the amount of white blood corpuscles had increased massively.

Repeated experiments like this have been producing similar results. The interest is so great that it has spawned a completely new area of medical research called psychoneuroimmunology (PNI). Not so long ago doctors would have protested against the idea that the immune system could be influenced by thought. Today therapies are successfully carried out in this field. For example, American scientists have developed video games for cancer patients in the course of which patients observe human killer T-cells and help them on the screen to destroy cancer cells.

Some surgeons meditate with patients, before they are about to undergo an organ transplantation. Using only the power of suggestion they can make the patient's body believe that a new kidney is a valuable gift. The patient's brain, it is believed, sends out messages to the immune system to minimise its reaction and so decrease the chances of rejection. For the same reasons, it is now common practice in some hospitals to send clowns and entertainers to the beds of child cancer patients.

The other side of the coin, not surprisingly, is that the mind can have a negative effect on the workings of the body. American biologist Robert Sapolsky has found that we produce stress hormones when we suffer depression, feel trapped or are under intense pressure. Stress hormones are released for a reason – they call up the last physical and psychological reserves of strength to turn us round the corner, to help relieve the tension, acting in a similar way to adrenalin when we're faced with a dangerous situation. In doing so, however, they destroy valuable nerve cells and, if called upon too often, can adversely affect our brain, causing it to age more rapidly. In severe cases, memory and learning ability have been impaired by up to 40%. As a remedy, Sapolsky proposes what he calls 'psychological disarmament'. In other words, think positive. Don't let the world get you down.

As Head of the Institute for Experimental Medicine and Surgery at the University of Montreal, Hans Selye began a series of experiments in the thirties which lead to a revolutionary discovery. Stress causes illness and early aging. Selye established that 'stress is a result of wear and tear in a biological system; it affects either the organism as a whole . . . or one of its parts.' He further discovered that stress is a condition which is caused by every activity in life and which, in a certain way, runs parallel to the intensity of life. Physical injury, nervous tension, hard work and infections all increase stress.

Selye carried out many experiments to support his theory, including investigations of the hormones released in the body during times of stress. According to his results, the body fights against stress by releasing increased amounts of ACTH (adrenocorticotropic hormone) in the hypophysis, and this in turn encourages the adrenal cortex to produce corticoid hormones.

Selye's claimed that every human being is born with a limited amount of this hormone. If you led a particularly hassled existence your reserves could be used up. Consequently, he reasoned, the process of physical aging does not only depend on your number of years but more on the extent to which your energy pool has been utilized.

In our society, stress is a major determining factor for illness and aging. Fortunately, we now know that not only can we reduce it, we can also increase our dwindling reserves of energy releasing hormones simply through the power of the mind.

Statistical investigations constantly offer new possibilities of delaying the aging process through non-medical means. A positive attitude to life, a desire to make the most of your lot, the fostering of a close circle of friends well into old age, engaging in stimulating activities, being part of a loving partnership, retaining physical and mental freshness, staying sexually active — all are stress relievers and life enhancers. And for those in old age, a reason to live is often more powerful than any medication. Those who shoulder responsibilities right up to their final years feel needed; those who look back on their long lives feeling at ease with themselves are more capable of looking forward too. Similarly, forming active groups among the older generation does not only positively affect their physical condition, but also supports their self-esteem. If you feel like you've been left on the scrap heap, your body might think so too.

It's all too easy to become melancholic about aging. But depression over those fleeting years – regarding each birthday as another step closer to the coffin – creates a self-fulfilling prophecy. The more we linger over it, the quicker age catches up with us. Besides 'old' is a relative term. The original meaning of the word, which derives from the Saxon 'alda', is merely 'grown-up'. And the term 'youth', which has meanwhile been built up into an object of worship, was valued very negatively by the Saxons, who often died young. Youth was synonymous with bad habits such as: uncontrolled behaviour, impetuousness, ignorance, immaturity, inexperience and other equally uncomplimentary characteristics. The moral? Age is a state of mind – the less it matters to you, the longer you'll last.

Some parts of our body wear down from overuse, others get stronger. If we are to keep our bodies in trim through positive thinking, then it follows that we must look after our brain as well. Luckily, results show that brains subjected to regular mental agility stay healthier, and keep going longer.

Scientists once assumed that the human brain loses 100000 nerve cell neurons every day. Therefore the intellectual capacity of a seventy year old would be reduced by at least 20% compared to its original capacity. Naturally, this caused widespread concern especially for those, like scientists themselves, whose very brains were their *raison d'etre*.

In the end, however, a mathematical error was responsible for all the trouble. The American anatomist

The Future

Harold Brody had worked out the amount of nerve cells of young and old brains per unit of area; according to his count, the brain of a ninety-five year old contained less than a third of the neurons in a new-born baby. The German neuro-anatomist Herbert Haug from the University of Lübeck, however, pointed out that younger tissue contains more water – which evaporates when being dissected. Brody had simply forgotten to consider this fact. As the brain shrinks with age, due to loss of fluid, the space between the neurons decreases. Under normal circumstances one cubic millimetre contains around 40 000 nerve cells. Brody had jumped to the erroneous conclusion that younger brains were superior to older ones.

Today we know that, overall, the potential of the human brain hardly changes up to about the age of sixty, although sections of the brain develop differently. While the capacity of the visual centre is preserved, the reactions of the locomotor system slow down. Memory and intelligence do not necessarily dwindle, as the potential of the brain is not dependent on the amount of neurons (and there is a huge, unused reserve of them anyway), but on the quality of the dendrites – tree-like branched plasma systems on the surface of the nerve cells – through which all the working neurons send their electrochemical signals. And dendrites continue to grow in very old people.

Some scientists are of the opinion that the evolutionary development of Homo sapiens could only take place, because we retained 'childlike' characteristics: eg curiosity, imagination, thirst for knowledge and endless energy. As a result neoteny, the process of remaining childlike, was responsible for the development of humans. This is why a young chimpanzee seems to possess more human characteristics than an old one.

Many aspects of our modern world don't allow these characteristics to flourish. Our mental abilities are channelled from an early age, skills and knowledge are specialised as soon as we embark on a career. Versatility is wasting away. Furthermore, for most of us the act of learning ceases, at latest, by the age of twenty-five – often a great deal earlier. We become ensnared in a one-dimensional working life instead of stretching our capabilities to the limit. And when we pack it in, many of us seem to pack life along with it. Retirement offers only fear, our days become vacuums. This, of course, is wrong. At all stages in our lives we should seek challenges – it's what our brains were designed for. If we don't use our brains, our brains might abuse us.

The rate of growth of scientific knowledge is doubling every five years. As we become embroiled in this exponential vortex of technology, it is imperative that we don't lose sight of our inherent human characteristics. Curiosity, fantasy and creativity are required in all age groups. For as old as we may become in future – be it eighty, two hundred, four hundred or one day even eight hundred years old – we should end our life, as late as possible, in a state of youthful freshness.

The untapped potential of the brain should not be underestimated. Western science has only recently begun to take notice of this. What was once arrogantly dismissed 'mysticism from the east' is now being taken seriously. In laboratory tests the astonishing abilities of meditating yogis and shamans were investigated with the help of the most modern measuring equipment.

The scientists were fascinated by stories of fakirs able to lie on beds of nails and piercing through their bodies with arrows and swords without feeling any pain, or stopping the bleeding of large cuts in a very short time by using meditative techniques. They'd heard of shamans who could force up their own body temperature by 'lighting the inner fire' and, completely clothed, enter water at near freezing temperatures. Within minutes of leaving the water, so went the reports, their clothing was totally dry due to the heat from their bodies. And then there were the tales, outlandish on the face of it, of Tibetan and Siberian shamans who could sink themselves into a state of suspended animation for a period of time.

The West suddenly wanted to know if there was any scientific basis for these claims. In experiments it was proved that experimentees in deep meditation produced brain waves – alpha waves – which in an electroencephalogram (EEG = measurement of the current in the brain) mostly show a state of relaxation. (A method, by which superlearning or supersporting is achieved. In this state, 1000 words of vocabulary can be absorbed daily in the subconscious and can so be stored in the long-term memory. In supersporting it is a matter of unconsciously rehearsing or of storing difficult sequences of movement, for example in fencing, tennis, golf, etc. These would then be easily managed when put into practice later on; similar to the zen archery of Buddhist monks, who after years of meditation can hit their target without aiming.) Relaxation through self-hypnosis, or even better, controlled biofeedback, is an effective technique for reaching this meditative alpha state. Linked to the EEG, and other monitoring equipment, the meditators' body reactions were recorded. It was found that on reaching the alpha state, the subjects could sink their body temperature by using the power of imagination.

In various further experiments, subjects were able to influence their bodily functions in the most amazing way with the help of deep self-hypnosis. Women increased the release of certain hormones by imagining an inner fire. The result: the size of their bosom increased by up to twelve centimetres.

Similar methods have been adopted overcome fear of flying. The patient had to imagine all the events which were part of a flight. The patient was only considered airworthy, once the control units no longer registered any signs of panic or fear. The close observation of the control units combined with the intense concentration of the subject were often enough to make all signs of the fear of flying gradually disappear.

The power of thought over physiological processes is shown in a most impressive way by another example. Scientists from the Michigan State University showed their experimentees slides of a certain type of cell whose activities and characteristics they described. After this, the experimentees were asked to imagine how these cells enter and then leave the blood circulation. The scientists established that their experimentees could reduce and increase the number of these cells, without impairing other types of cells. In another test the experimentees were set the task of changing the amount of the cells which become fixed on the walls of the blood vessels. It turned out that the experimentees were able to successfully master their task simply by calling on their own willpower.

William Braud from the Mind Science Foundation in San Antonio, Texas, tested how far humans are able to 'have an effect' on the blood of other people simply by using intense mental concentration. In an experiment, it was shown that the influencing person could determine the speed at which the red blood corpuscles in the blood of the other test person dissolved.

Everyone knows the saying 'faith can move mountains'. Well, when it comes to the health of the body if you replace the word 'faith' with 'meditation' or 'willpower' it certainly appears to be true. No scientist, as yet, has come up with a sure fire way of curing illness simply through utilising the power of the mind. Willpower alone may not be enough – but it is an essential component in our armoury against illness and aging. All too often when we speak of psychosomatic recoveries it always seems to be slightly disparaging. 'Oh, it was just psychosomatic. The treatment didn't really work.' 'Just'? He was cured by the power of his own mind and this is to be dismissed lightly? Positive thinking is one of the most powerful weapons we have against all sorts of diseases. If you think you're going to get better, it increases your chances of actually doing so. There are even documented reports of cancer being cured this way. Attitude is vitally important if you are severely ill, because all the medication in the world is unlikely to help if your mind and soul have given up the fight.

If you want to be around for the next few hundred years, imprint this motto on your brain: Keep smiling, keep thinking – be *alive*.

CHAPTER TEN

The Yogis' Secret

From time immemorial the snowy mountains of the Himalayas have been considered to be the home of the gods. This majestic mountain range stretches over a length of about 1500 miles. Its peaks are the highest in the world, many of them rising over 26 000 feet. The word Himalaya comes from Sanskrit and is made up of the words 'hima' (snow) and 'palayap' (home) – 'home of the snow'.

For most of the inhabitants of the Indian subcontinent the Himalayas mean much more than that. The range is also called the 'roof of the world' and represents, in mythology, the foothills of the legendary Mount Meru, the axis mundi, on which the firmament rests. According to Hindu beliefs, here, where heaven and earth meet, the Gods come down to earth and meet those people who have spent their lives seeking religious enlightenment. Hindus consider the Himalayas to be the kingdom of the God Shiva, who meditates at the foot of his holy mountain Kailash and undertakes expeditions together with his followers. It is said that the Ganga – the Ganges, as we call it – the holiest river in India, rises from his home.

The Hindus believe that bathing in the Ganga purifies the soul and improves the karma, the 'life's work' of all incarnations that an individual has experienced up to now. As a kind of final balance of the good and bad deeds, the karma decides the quality of the next incarnation in the eternal circle of death and rebirth. Hindus make pilgrimages in their thousands to the holy city of Benares or to Rishikesh high up in the mountains to make sure that their next incarnation will be one which holds a promise of happiness.

The God Shiva, guardian of the holy Ganga, is also the patron of the yogis and sadhus, the holy men of India, who try to become at one with the brahma, the soul of the world, by using special techniques of meditative contemplation. Their highest principle is the love of creation. They make pilgrimages to Rishikesh, the site where in ancient times the seven Rishis (seers) received the Vedas (the holy scriptures of India).

From Rishikesh they push further into the highlands – always following the Ganga, so as to be as near as possible to its source. They live there in caves, and their possessions often only consist of a loincloth and a statue of their favourite god, usually Shiva, or his son Ganesa with the head of an elephant.

Many have also devoted themselves to the god Krishna, the young shepherd from Brindavan, who is said to be the incarnation of the god Vishnu, the sustainer of the world. It was he, who on the battlefield of Kurukshetra explained the Bhagavad-Gita, the bible of India, to his pupil Arjuna. This book, in which the four ways of yoga are shown, discloses to the seeker the way out of the eternal circle of death and rebirth.

Innumerable legends have grown up around these sadhus and yogis and around the mystical abilities they have gained through practising yoga, inner contemplation and harnessing the hidden powers within the human form. These magical powers of the yogis are called siddhis and the yogi gains them by collection ('samyama').

The following siddhis are listed in the ancient textbook of yoga, the *Yoga Sutura* by the Indian wiseman Patanjali (2 BC):

— Aitta-anagata-jnanam: knowledge of what happened in the past and what will happen in the future;

— Sarvabhuta-ruta-jnanam: familiarity with the language of all living beings;

— Purva-jati-jnanam: familiarity with earlier existences;

— Para-citta-jnanam: knowledge of the thoughts of others;

— Apara-anta-jnanam: prediction of one's own death or accident;

— Tad-grahya-sakti-stamphe caksuh-prakasa-asamyogenntardhanam: the power to interrupt the connection between eye and light and make oneself invisible;

— Balesu hasti-bala-adini: possession of the strength of an elephant;

— Suksma-vyavahita-viprakrsta-jnanam: knowledge of subtle, hidden or far-off things;

— Bhuvana-jnanam: knowledge of the secrets of the cosmos;

— Tara-vyuha-jnanam: knowledge of the order of the stars;

— Kaya-vyuha-jnanam: knowledge of the inner order of the body;

— Ksut-pipasa-nivrttih: the ability to make hunger and thirst disappear;

— Pratibhadva sarvam: the ability to recognize everything in a flash of intuition;

— Ca cittasya parasarira-avesah: the ability to slip into other bodies;

— Jala-panka-kantaka-adisu asanga utkrantis ca: the ability to walk through water, mud or thorns, without coming into contact with them and leaving the body there;

— Laghu-tula-samapattes ca akasa-gamanam: the ability to make the body as light as cotton and float freely in space;

— Tatonnima-adi-pradurvhavah kaya-sampat taddharma-anabhighatas ca: the ability to reduce the body to the size of an atom; perfection and invulnerability of the body.

It is said that these mystical abilities assure the yogi constant health, bodily strength and a long life. And there are supposedly yogis in the caves of the Himalayas who are several hundred years old. One of these legendary and almost immortal wisemen is Swami Sarvesvarananda, whose name means 'rapture by mastering nature'. He was apparently born in the 14th century and would therefore have to be over six hundred and fifty years old. His cave, which is at a height of about 22 300 feet, is in a barren and infertile area, in which the temperatures sometimes fall to −40C. Nevertheless he is almost totally naked, lives only off the water from melting snow and does not even eat vegetable food. That, at least, is what his pupil Sri Ram Sharma Acarya Maharaj claims, whose ashram (monastic school) Shanti Kunj is on the outskirts of Hardwar on the old pilgrim's road between Rishikesh and Badrinath.

While we only know the legendary Swami Sarvesvarananda from the accounts of Sri Ram − who at least brought back a photo of his master after visiting him in his hermitage − the acarya (teacher) is himself an impressive example for the longevity of yogis. For although Sri Ram is proven to be 86 years old, he is full of energy and captivates his pupils, predominantly Indians, but occasionally visitors from the west, for hours with his teachings.

Sri Ram Maharaj was born in 1908 into a Brahman family, which lived in the region of Agra, famous for its Taj Mahal. His father, Sri Rupam Sharma, was a good friend of Motilal, the father of Pandit Nehru, first president of India and a close friend of Gandhi.

As a young boy Sri Ram received the gayatri initiation and yajnopavitram, the award of the Brahman braid.

Besides this, as a lad, he practiced vedmata japa, the reciting of vedish hymns. Then one day an imposing, naked yogi with kind eyes, long hair and a long wavy beard appeared to him in a vision. He immediately felt that this was his teacher, his guru and that he had to set off to find him. A long pilgrimage finally led him to the other side of Badrinath to a mountain hermitage called Tapovan (place of spiritual abstinence). There he met a British colonel, L.P. Farrell, who told him of a legendary yogi, whose pupil he had become. Together with the colonel he set off into the mountains – and found Swami Sarvesvarananda, who accepted him as a pupil and instructed him to immediately carry out a hard spiritual exercise.

For the next thirty years Sri Ram fasted, eating only Bajri-roti and butter-milk. Innumerable times he recited the holy Gayatri-Mantra of the Hindus, the most famous prayer of hinduism:

Om bhur bhuvah svaha
tat savitur varenyam
bhargo devasya dhimahi
dhiyo yo nah pracodayat.

O transcendental reality,
which exists in the heart of the earth,
in the life of heaven and
in the soul of the universe,
praiseworthy, omnipotent, divine mother,
Godly light, to which we mediate,
enlighten our mind and intellect.

Again and again Swami Sarvesvarananda visited his pupil's hermitage at the foot of the Himalayas, where he translated and explained ancient holy texts. In 1971, Sri Ram opened his ashram in Hardwar, which he runs with his female companion Mata Bhagwati Devi.

As unbelievable as the story of the immortal Swami Sarvesvarananda may seem, it is not the exception. Almost every summer another yogi, Devraha Baba, makes a pilgrimage from the east of the Indian State Uttar Pradesh to a shrine in Hardwar at the foot of the Himalayas. Dr. Rajendra Prasad, claims that he can prove from his own experience that Devraha Baba is over one hundred and fifty years old. For when he was a young boy, his father took him to the Baba, who at that time was already a very old man.

'When I was your age, my father brought me to Baba,' the father of young Rajendra told him at this opportunity. 'He carries the strength of God in him, that is why he never dies.' Dr. Prasad was already over seventy, when he told this story.

'He lives mostly in wooden huts and treehouses,' writes author Swami Rama, describing his meeting with Devraha Baba in his book *Living with Himalayan Masters*. 'He looked very healthy and seemed to be in his seventies. Although he himself is very strict and religious and allows none of his pupils to touch him, he sometimes organises discourses about divine love. He is very well-known in northern India and when he gives his darshanas (audiences), great crowds of people gather. He has a huge following and even policemen and government officials come and ask him for his blessing. One of my American pupils visited him in Hardwar in 1974 during the Kumbha Mela, a religious festival, which takes place every twelve years. I tried to find out his secret of long life and discovered that he regularly does certain yoga exercises and only lives from fruit and vegetables. There is a whole series of corresponding yoga exercises. During my conversation with Baba he said: "The greatest wealth lies in happiness. Regularity is essential. Practising advanced techniques is as important as breathing. Not aging is a technique of the pranayama."'

Pranayama or the 'control of pranas' (energy of life) is an ancient breathing technique of the yogi. It is based on the idea that apart from fire, water, earth and air there is a fifth element called prana or ether, which can best be translated as vitality. It is absorbed with breath and diverted into the nadis, the nerve pathways of the human body. There are three main channels: ida, pingala and sushumna, as well as thousands of small side channels.

Prana flows through the left-hand side of the body with the help of ida, through the right-hand side by means of pingala, and along the spine through the spinal cord due to sushumna. Ida is breathed in through the left nostril, pingala through the right, sushumna, when we breath in through both nostrils. As with the snakes on the staff of Asclepius, ida, pingala and sushumna meet in six different places along the spine. These convergences are energy centres called chakras (wheels).

A seventh chakra also exists in the vertex area. Every chakra has a colour, sound and a characteristic, which vary according to tradition.

Sanskrit name	Colour	Sound	Characteristic
Root chakra muladhara	orange	si	life and death
Spleen chakra svadhisthana	blood red	la	sexuality
Navel chakra manipura	green	sol	emotions
Heart chakra anahata	gold	fa	love
Larynx chakra visuddha	blue	mi	communication
Forehead chakra ajna	pink	re	intellect
Vertex chakra sahasrara	violet	do	spirituality

The aim of the kundalini yoga system, to which the breathing technique pranayama belongs, is to open these chakras. The yogis believe that when this happens unimaginable psychological abilities are released. A Western representative of yoga teachings, the renowned meditation teacher Sri Chinmoy, who teaches peace meditation at the United Nations, attributes truly marvellous things to it:

'If you have attained control over the muladhara chakra, you can make yourself invisible just as you wish and you can overcome all illnesses. You learn everything you wish to learn and discover everything you would like to discover . . .

'If you possess the mastery of the svadhisthana chakra, you attain the power of love. You love everyone and are loved by all, by men and by animals . . .

'Whoever controls manipura, the navel chakra, defeats worry and suffering . . .

'A seeker, who possesses control over the anahata centre, has free access to the visible and invisible worlds. Time and space are his subjects. If he uses this centre of power, then in his astral body he can travel to any place in the world within a few seconds . . .

'Whoever controls the visuddha chakra, has the ability to convey divine messages to the world. Universal nature reveals age-old hidden secrets to him. Nature bows to the seeker. He can maintain eternal youth . . .

'Ajna, the forehead chakra, helps those who control it to boundless spiritual and occult powers . . .

'Sahasrara, the vertex chakra, lets the person, who is able to open it, permanently enjoy endless bliss. He becomes inseparably one with the eternally transcending after-world and recognises that he is free of birth and death. He then only lives in endlessness, eternity and immortality.' (From *Kundalini* by Sri Chinmoy)

The American psychologist Dr. Elmar Green from the renowned Menniger Foundation in Topeka Kansas argues that these yogic abilities should not be scoffed at. Green is one of world's leading experts on biofeedback and the control of the inner bodily functions by the psyche. Fascinated by the claims of the Indian yogis he decided to, in his words, 'get wise to' their mystical abilities using scientific means. He therefore invited the Indian yogi Swami Rama to the USA, in order to investigate the effects of his meditations on the body. The experiments took place in the biofeedback laboratories at the Menniger Foundation.

Swami Rama demonstrated his control of the arteries in his wrist, by warming the palm of his hand in one place and cooling down another place only five centimetres away, until there was a difference of temperature of 4C between the two areas. Furthermore, he managed to reduce his heartbeat, monitored by the ECG, from 70 to 52 beats in less than one minute!

After that the yogi offered to stop his heart beating completely for three to four minutes. Dr. Green said that ten seconds would be enough to prove that it is possible. In the experiment room Swami Rama was connected to the electrodes that linked his heartbeat to the ECG. In the control room Dr. Ferguson and Dr. Sargent, two doctors from the Menninger Foundation, watched the experiment through a window. The heartbeat actually stopped. After Swami Rama had put himself into yogic meditation, the ECG showed a slight flickering of the heart. But after seventeen seconds the observers became uneasy and ordered the experiment to be stopped, because they feared that the yogi could suffer lasting damage to his health.

Such amazing feats are rarely observed but have been documented before. In the 19th century the yogi Haridas was said to have put himself into a state of suspended animation for forty days using a completely different method, hatha yoga. Yogi Haridap's experiment became known in the West from the report 'Observations on trance or human Hibernation' written by J. Braids in 1850.

According to Braids, Haridas followed an ancient method in which the tongue band is cut at the lower tongue root and the tongue is pulled until it touches the eyebrows. To achieve the state of complete trance the tongue is then bent back, so that the entrance to the windpipe is totally closed off. Only after this, can a state of suspended animation be reached. According to the report the hatha yogi Haridas let himself, in front of eyewitnesses, be buried in this condition for forty days in the garden of a maharajah, who doubted his abilities. The burial was carried out with the greatest of precautions by soldiers of the muslim faith, who were more than hostile to the Hindu yogi. They put him in a grave, which was filled in and covered up with a heavy stone slab. To exclude any kind of deception, the building containing the grave was also bricked up.

True to the yogi's instructions the building was broken open exactly forty days later and the stone slab was pushed to one side. He was dug out, after which one of his pupils woke him.

Observers assured that no signs of bodily functions were found in his 'grave'. He was however extremely dehydrated.

In 1961, three renowned Indian physiologists, Drs. Anand, Chhina and Singh examined a yogi at their laboratory, in a closed and sealed air-tight glass case. The yogi remained in the case for ten hours while researchers from time to time tested the air in it for its oxygen content. They found to their astonishment that this yogi managed the whole time on an amount of oxygen roughly 30% lower than the absolute minimum considered necessary for life. For a while, half way through the experiment, he only used 50% of the absolute minimum. Nevertheless, the yogi suffered no harm after it was over.

In another study the Indian neurophysiologists Drs. Bagchi and Wenger recorded the bodily functions of fifty-five experimentees meditating in a yoga position. During meditation their heart rate sank 6-9% and their respiratory frequency was reduced by 23%. In some cases breathing even decreased by 50-60% and was at times so shallow that it could not be measured. For some, one or two breaths per minute were sufficient. At the same time an increase in the electrical skin resistance – generally a sign for diminishing stress – was noted. The brain patterns of the experimentees showed extremely strong, distinctive patterns of alpha waves.

Brain rhythms are indicated by their frequency, that means by a certain number of cycles or peaks per second. Alpha rhythms are measured at the back of the head and show between eight and twelve cycles per second. Theta rhythms are even slower – five to seven cycles per second. Both of these different brain waves have a special importance for neurologists, as they apparently only appear in connection with specific mental conditions. Alpha waves show sleepiness and deep mental relaxation. Theta waves usually appear just before going to sleep. Some researchers are of the opinion that creative people receive their most important inspirations in the theta state. Alpha waves are characteristic for the state of meditation, while theta waves only appear after alpha waves in people who are very experienced meditators.

Drs. Anand, Chhina and Singh were especially interested in finding out how these alpha patterns reacted to noises and sensory disturbances. The yogis claim that in the samadhi condition of deep contemplation they don't register outer stimuli at all, as they are in an ecstatic state of bliss — sat-chit-ananda (existence-consciousness-bliss). The researchers therefore decided to subject their experimentees in the samadhi state to bright light, loud noises, touching their skin with a hot glass tube, hitting a tuning fork next to their ears, or dipping hands in ice cold water in an attempt to stimulate the sense organs. When an alpha state is disturbed it normally shows signs of interruption for a time and another pattern takes its place. According to experience, repeating a stimulus leads to a habituation effect. The alpha rhythm of the yogis was also interrupted, but here there was no such habituation effect. Whenever a stimulus was repeated, the alpha rhythm of the yogis reacted as if it was being interrupted by this stimulus for the first time, they had simply not registered it before.

A different picture emerged when the yogis reached the samadhi state. The EEG unit showed alpha waves with increasing oscillation swings. As the waves became deeper and more rhythmical, the distracting stimuli were repeated. But however intensive they were, it now had no effect. It appeared that the meditators in the samadhi state were perfectly immune to outside sensory interference. Nevertheless, none of the experimentees showed the usual patterns of sleep, mentally they remained wide awake.

In a similar test in the research laboratory at the Menninger Foundation in Topeka the yogi Swami Rama surprised psychologists when, after finishing his meditation, he was able to repeat what they had said during the tests – often verbatim – even though he had, according to the EEG, been in the samadhi state.

Over and above all this, the neurologists and psychologists established the following from their yogi experiments: Unlike during sleep, the alpha waves show unusually regular and rhythmical wave forms during meditation. In addition these alpha waves did not only tend to spread out from the back to the front of the brain, but they also brought about a synchronisation (phase coincidence) of both sides of the brain. Meditation therefore does not only produce a rhythmic pattern in the place of the otherwise aimless and chaotic brain waves of normal consciousness, it also activates the left-hand rational side of the brain and the right-hand intuitive half of the brain at the same time. By fusing them together, as it were, deep meditation allows the 'whole' person to emerge, together with a wide spectrum of abilities previously undiscovered.

In all probability pranayama and meditation are a key to one of the locks on the door barring the way to a long, healthy and integral life. Isn't that reason enough to have a look at both methods more closely?

Pranayama is one of the oldest yoga techniques. Controlling breathing and with it the 'vital airs' in the body is used to clean the nervous currents (nadis) in the body and to activate the chakras. Through activation, the paranormal powers attributed to these chakras, are developed. At the same time the kundalini ('snake power'), which has its place in the root chakra, is aroused. This must be raised up to the highest chakra, the sahasrara. In this way the yogi reaches enlightenment, the complete activation of all the powers of humankind and to the ability to become one, absolutely and meditatively, with the areas of consciousness and creation.

In order to reach this aim, kundalini yoga has developed a systematic technique, in which special attention is paid to place, length, speed, depth and the rhythms of breathing. Under normal circumstances human breathing is very random, breathing in and out takes place irregularly and unharmoniously. Yoga teaches that man breathes in and out 21 600 times a day. But most of the breaths are shallow and rapid and therefore do not provide the body with enough energy. Moreover, as the lungs themselves are often only filled to a fraction of their capacity, the energy current is too slight to activate the kundalini.

The first step of pranayama consists of breathing in a certain way and keeping to a rhythm when breathing in and out. For rhythmical control prevents energy dissipation, supports concentration and calms the impulses of the autonomic nervous system. In this way the prevailing mood of the body is improved and the inner functions of our psycho-physical organism become better coordinated with each other.

Pranayama is practised in connection with other yoga practices such as asana (seating position), mudra (hand positions, finger gestures), bandha (inner muscle contraction), and many other variations and combinations to increase life energy.

The learning of pranayama consists of several phases. The basic requirement is conscious breathing and attentive observation of the breathing sequence. When the flow of prana becomes noticeable, it is time to begin with controlled breathing. The next step is asana, the body position. The position, in which the prana energy can flow along the sushumna unhindered is the 'padmasana', also known as the lotus position. You sit with crossed legs and place the left foot on the right thigh and the right foot on the left thigh. Siddhasana, the 'position of perfection' is the ideal, where the right heel is firmly pressed onto the perineum and the left heel is placed on the right thigh, touching the abdomen.

In both positions an upright posture is especially important, if anything to stop tiredness developing. The eyes are focused on the tip of the nose – not cross-eyed – and the hands are placed on the knees. The yogis claim that the triangular forms created by this position, build up a closed field from which the currents of energy cannot escape, but rather remain within the body circulation.

As soon as you have mastered the correct position, the next step is to take in a maximum of prana in your breathing, while keeping the rhythm constant. A unit of breathing is made up of three phases, breathing in (puraka), holding breath (kumbhaka) and breathing out (recaka). A balanced relationship must be established between these three phases where, according to yogic writings, a ratio of 1:4:2 is supposed to be the optimum. In seconds that means the following:

Breathing in	Holding breath	Breathing out	Resting
4	16	8	1
6	24	12	2
8	32	16	3

In the next phase, air is slowly breathed in through the left nostril, which is connected to the ida channel, while the other one is kept closed with the thumb. Hold the breath and breathe out, as the special rhythm prescribes. Now the exercise is repeated by keeping the left nostril closed with the index finger and breathing in through the right. To measure the sequence of time the sound 'OM' should be repeated frequently – in the following ratio 1:4:2.

In a further exercise you should keep the left nostril closed when breathing in, and the right one when breathing out. Then do the reverse. In addition it is recommended to concentrate on both the nerve currents, ida and pingala, as well as their continued rhythmical flow impulses in all pranayama meditations. You should be able to feel how the kundalini are aroused by the transmitted flow impulses.

After a pranayama exercise, it is recommended that you lie flat on your back 'like a corpse'. This position is called savasana and is conducive to a state of calm. The number of exercises should steadily increase both in duration and complexity. If you hold your breath for a longer period of time, then the system can accept more energy until, the ultimate aim, your body comes into harmony with its inner elements.

'The face glows like a sun,' it says in the sutras, the old yogi scriptures, and 'finally the seeker feels how the prana runs through the sushumna and arouses the kundalini.' On reaching this stage, the seeker should concentrate on the third eye, the ajna chakra, or the heart chakra, as, of all the chakras, it is the safest and most satisfying to arouse first.

Pranayama has another function through yoga: it is the optimal preparation for the art of contemplation. It is the focusing on one single sensory stimulus, the object of concentration. The meditator steers attention to the Absolute or, as the Indians would say, the Divine in the ultimate aim to be united with it.

There are numerous methods and schools of mediation, but the generally recognised founder of the discipline is the classic textbook *Yoga Sutra* from the wiseman Patanjali, who lived in the second century BC. 'Asceticism, study and devotion to God make up the yoga of action (kriya yoga)' Patanjali wrote. 'The aim of yoga is meditation and contemplation to reduce tensions . . . Non-violence, truthfulness, not stealing, a pure way of life and non-acquisition are the rules of outer discipline . . . Pureness, peace, asceticism, study and devotion to God are the inner order.' The seating position should be firm and comfortable. It should be assumed in complete relaxation and in a state of consideration of the infinite. From that, an immunity to the pairs of opposites follows.

These pairs of opposites are the polarities of the material world: light and darkness, heat and cold, night and day. 'If you are deeply rooted in this state, then the regulation of breathing (pranayama) follows, which is a pause in the rhythm of breathing in and out. It consists of the procedures of breathing out, breathing in and holding your breath, and it is long or subtle, if place, length and passing of time are observed. The fourth form of pranayama goes beyond the outer and inner values. In this way the veil, which lies over the inner enlightenment is removed. The ability to concentrate the thoughts is now possible. When the senses draw away from the objections of the mind, this state becomes pratyahara (restraint of the senses), leading to perfect control of the senses. The continued existence of the consciousness in the emptiness of the room is concentration [dharana].

'Dharana is also experienced through the consciousness being close to the object of contemplation by attuning oneself into a single act of experience, meditation [dhyana]. Only through meditation, which leads to enlightenment, in the course of which one is robbed of identity as it were, can we truly practice samadhi [contemplation].'

In samadhi the object fuses with the subject, the meditator exposes his ego and becomes part of the whole, and so attains cosmic consciousness. The person who can reach this state has gained true immortality. He has become one with creation and has freed himself from the circle of death and reincarnation. But it is a long road to this state, and one which demands strict discipline.

Anyone who wants to start meditation should first prepare themselves for regularity and discipline. The Brahma muhurti ('hour of God') which is 4 am, may not correspond to the rhythm of a working Westerner, but the Indians do stress that 6 o'clock in the morning, midday and 6 o'clock in the evening are also well suited to meditation. Nature wakes in the morning hours, holds its breath and allows itself a break at lunchtime and comes to rest in the evening. It is important to meditate with an empty stomach. Semi-luxuries such as tea, coffee and, of course alcohol, should be avoided at least two hours before starting to meditate.

Choose a quiet room and make sure that you remain undisturbed. Disconnect the telephone. Meditate in a light corner, maybe next to a plant – if only for the fresher air – and arrange everything so that you feel settled: Comfortable clothing is essential, and if you have not mastered the yoga sitting position (or find it uncomfortable), sit up straight on a comfortable chair and take your shoes off. The period of meditation should be between ten and twenty minutes. You can put a quiet clock in your line of vision to make sure.

The yoga novice should first of all begin with concentration exercises. When doing such an exercise it is usual to light a candle and focus on the flame. With controlled concentration deviating thoughts can be increasingly eliminated, and the outer world is excluded for a short time. If you are still plagued by thoughts, you can imagine that these are being led into the flame and burned. This exercise is more difficult than it first appears. Those practising it, especially when they try to remove their mind from the hectic nature of our modern world, will be astonished at how many thoughts go through their minds and how difficult it is to concentrate on one single object for a long time. Every time your attention is distracted, it must again be brought back to the flame. Controlled breathing, even without complicated pranayama rhythms, will help. When breathing in, try to imagine a current of energy, which flows from the flame to your heart, and which returns to the flame when breathing out. But only after regular practise will you experience moments in which the contrast between yourself and the candle is removed, in which subject and object fuse into one.

Another exercise, which is well suited for those starting meditation, is the concentration on a mantra, a holy word, to whose sound vibration a certain power is attributed. 'OM', the ancient syllable of Hindu cosmology, the 'sound of God', is a wide-spread mantra, but 'So-Ham' (I am) is also well suited, especially if the 'So' is hummed when breathing in and the 'Ham' when breathing out. As meditating with your eyes closed can quickly lead to a dozy state or even to nodding off, it is recommended to meditate with the eyes half-closed, with your mind fixed on the inner space between the eyebrows (the third eye).

While these exercises are completely safe and can be done by everyone, yoga experts do advise instruction by an experienced teacher for more complicated methods. Almost all of those, who practise yoga swear that these simple and not particularly time-consuming exercises have made their lives healthier, more harmonious and more creative. And maybe they are the way to the highest aim, which an ancient Hindu mantra describes as follows:

> Asato ma sad gamaya
> Tamaso ma jyotir gamaya
> Mrtyor ma amrtam gamaya
>
> Lead me from the unreal to reality,
> Lead me from darkness to light,
> Lead me from death to immortality.

CHAPTER ELEVEN

Testing Times

What follows are a number of guidance points, check-lists, self-tests and assessments designed by researchers interested in the links between lifestyle and longevity. They are not exhaustive and should be not be considered as a comprehensive medical check-up. If you are in any doubt about your health, consult a GP or specialist as soon as possible. Having said that, taken together they are a very useful tool for looking honestly at yourself and highlighting areas where you really could make improvements in your lifestyle. The majority of people, even fit healthy people, aren't maximising their potential. A balance in all areas – nutrition, exercise, lifestyle and mental outlook – is essential if you are to reap the rewards of the Methuselah Formula.

General guidance on diet and exercise

- Only eat, when you are really hungry. Appetite is usually mistaken for hunger and is often just habit. Real hunger is a physiological sign.

- Don't eat when excited or tired.

- Avoid drinking with meals. Drink half an hour before you eat or several hours after you have eaten.

- Chew carefully.

- Do without sweets, cakes and pastries, white sugar, lemonade, cola drinks and similar.

- Favour the fruits and vegetables in season and eat these raw whenever possible.

- Eat little meat and meat products.

- Miss out a meal now and again. (Important – this *means* now and again. It is a not medical license to starve yourself.)

- Meat and vegetables shouldn't be overcooked. It is tastier and healthier to steam food under low heat with fine, preferably pressed vegetable oil (extra virgin olive oil is excellent) and very little liquid.

- You should spend at least one to two hours a day doing easy sports or working in the garden in the fresh air.

Vitamin Deficiency Checklist

The following symptoms were established in every age group and existed in both city and rural environments. Research has shown that they are mainly due to poor nutrition and lack of vitamins.

Please observe yourself as objectively as possible. Be honest and don't gloss over anything. Put a tick next to all the characteristics and problems which apply to you. If you recognize two or more symptoms you should try a good multivitamin preparation over a long period of time. If the list reveals more than five positive symptoms, then you should consult your doctor and seek detailed advice on how to alleviate them.

General bodily features
Thinness ☐
Retarded growth ☐
Obesity ☐
Muscular atrophy ☐
Withered, inelastic flesh ☐
Poor posture ☐
Round shoulders ☐
A dent remains in your skin long
   after pressing it ☐
Protruding stomach (pot belly) ☐
Thin, flat-chested ☐
Lack of coordination ☐

Facial expressions
Strained ☐
Worried ☐
Manically happy then deeply stressed ☐

State of the skin
- Waxen ☐
- Constant and chronic goose-pimples ☐
- Grey ☐
- Loose ☐
- Torn corner of the mouth ☐
- Rough ☐
- Dry ☐

Tongue – teeth – mouth
- Open cuts on tongue ☐
- Swollen tongue ☐
- Furred and furrowed tongue ☐
- Bright red tongue ☐
- Shiny tip of the tongue ☐
- Burning tongue ☐
- Pale gums ☐
- Bleeding gums ☐
- Puffy gums ☐
- Poor teeth ☐
- Missing teeth ☐
- Inflammation in the mouth ☐
- No teeth ☐

Eyes and lids
- Enlarged veins in the eyeball ☐
- Thin, strained mucous membranes ☐
- Red eyes ☐
- Tired eyes ☐
- Weeping eyes ☐
- Burning eyes ☐
- Encrustation around the eyes ☐
- Bags under the eyes ☐
- Eyelids flutter under bright light ☐

Dull eyes ☐
Styes on the lids ☐

Hair
Prematurely grey ☐
Dull hair ☐
Hair colour changed ☐
Dandruff ☐
Dry hair ☐
Excessive loss of hair ☐
Brittle hair ☐

General
Hectic ('flappy') ☐
Restless ☐
Apathetic ☐
Dizzy spells ☐
Depressive ☐
Fits of general weakness ☐
Lack of concentration ☐
Insomnia ☐
Fits of exhaustion ☐
Sensitive joints ☐
Lack of resistance to infection ☐
Delayed healing of wounds ☐
Lack of stamina ☐
Nose bleeds ☐
Brittle fingernails ☐
Listlessness ☐
Weak vitality ☐
Moody ☐
Constant tiredness ☐
Touchy ☐
Quarrelsome ☐

Trembling hands ☐
Poor memory ☐
Tendency to brood without any reason ☐
Sensitive to cold ☐
Chronic headaches ☐
Nervous ☐
Leg cramps during the night ☐

Digestion
Poor digestion ☐
Nervous digestive disorders ☐
Excessively choosy about food ☐
Flatulence ☐
Stomach pains ☐
Indigestibility of certain meals ☐
Gastric ulcers ☐
Constipation ☐

Mental attitude checklist

Are you old? This is not a matter of calendar years, but a state of mind. If you feel old, you are more likely to physically get older sooner according to scientific investigations in the USA. Check yourself against the following statements and see if you have a positive attitude towards what life holds for you now and what it may do in the future. You may be surprised by your answers.

1) You believe that you have learnt everything that you need to.

2) You have already caught yourself saying, 'I'm too old for that.'

3) You feel that the future holds little hope.

4) You are no longer interested in youthful pranks, and find them rather silly.

5) You prefer to talk rather than listen.

6) You long for the 'good old days,' which you consider to be the best, and dwell on nostalgia.

7) You aren't particularly helpful to your friends, to your neighbours or to society.

8) You have no thought-out plans for the future.

9) You often argue the point even when you know you're wrong, because deep down you want to be right.

If you agreed with any of these statements, don't worry – almost everybody does. It shows that there is always room for positive self-improvement. If you agreed with most of them then you need to examine your approach to life. Once people realize that life is for the living and not the wishing, they often live longer. It is not a question of living for many years, but above all of giving the years life and enjoying them. With a positive mental attitude, you can be aware of the influences which shorten life and find ways to control them. If you don't have the will to live, you are statistically more likely to live for a shorter time. Whatever your calendar years, if you keep looking to the future while enjoying the present you're more likely to be doing it longer than your morose neighbour next door.

The Holmes Test – changes in circumstance and stress levels

Dr. Thomas Holmes, professor of psychiatry at the University of Washington, has worked out a scale which allocates points for the various positive and negative changes which influence us throughout the course of our lives. From the section of the population that he observed, he concluded the following: if so many changes take place within a year that a total of 300 points or more is reached then a dangerous limit has been exceeded. According to Holmes' research 80% of those who had reached more than 300 points became ill with serious depressions, suffered heart attacks or other serious illnesses. The lower your total, the better the omens for a long and healthy life.

Event	Points
Death of husband or wife	100
Divorce	73
Separation	65
Prison sentence	63
Death of a close member of the family	63
Personal injury or illness	53
Marriage	50
Unemployment	47
Attempts to settle marital difficulties	45
Retirement	45
Family member falling ill	44

Pregnancy	40
Sexual difficulties	39
An addition to the family	39
Sever financial loss	38
Death of a close friend	37
Career change	36
Strong argument/disagreement with husband or wife	35
Credit due for repayment	30
Change of responsibility at work	29
A child leaves the family home	29
Trouble with the in-laws	29
Important personal achievements	28
Partner changes job	26
Beginning or finishing school	26
Change in personal habits	24
Trouble with boss	23
Moving home	20
Changing schools	20
Holidays	13
Slight infringements of the law	1

The Longevity Potential Test

The American National Institute on Aging and employees of the magazine *Longevity* have worked out the following test. It should help to check your prospects of a hopefully long and energetic life by using the listed system of points. The test contains seventeen key factors, which are divided into six main categories. Simply subtract or add the number of points to the next factor. At the end of the test you will find hints as to how you can work out the total number of points and how good or bad your chances are of living a life of above average length.

The Longevity Potential Test is presented with the kind permission of Longevity, copyright © 1990, Longevity International, Ltd.

A Habits
1. Tobacco (1 pipe = 2 cigarettes;
  1 cigar = 3 cigarettes)

Never smoked	+20
Stopped smoking	+10
Smoke up to a packet a day	−10
Smoke between one and two packets a day	−20
Smoke more than two packets a day	−30

Total consumption (Number per day)
Packets smoked per day x number of years
  in which you have smoked:

7 to 15	−5
16 to 25	−10
over 25	−20

2. Alcohol
(One beer or one glass of wine = 35 g
  of alcohol)

35 grammes of alcohol daily or less	+10
Between 35 and 70 g daily	−4

(One minus point more for every
  additional 35 g alcohol per day)   ____

3. Exercise
(20 minutes or more moderate aerobics)

3 x per week or more often	+20
Twice a week	+10
no regular aerobic activities	−10

Work demands regular physical exercise
   or at least a 2 mile walk   +3
(One additional point for every extra mile
   walked per day)   ____

4. Weight
   Ideal weight corresponding to height   +5
      5-10 lb above the ideal weight   −1
      11-20 lb above the ideal weight   −2
      21-30 lb above the ideal weight   −3
   (One additional minus point for every 10
      pounds above the ideal weight)   ____
   Yo-Yo-Diet   −10

5. Diet
   Eat balanced food   +3
   Don't eat balanced food   −3
   Eat regular meals at the same time every day +2
   Don't keep to regular meals at the same
      time every day   −2
   Eat snacks or meals during the night   −2
   Eat a balanced breakfast   +2
   Eat fish or poultry as main protein source
      (complete replacement for red meat)   +5
   Eat neither fish nor cereals as main
      source of protein   −2
   Eat green-leaved vegetables at least five
      times a week   +3
   Eat fresh fruit or drink fruit juice at least
      five times a week   +3
   Try to avoid fats   +3
   Don't try to avoid fats   −5

Assess the food in the following list, if you eat them twice a week or more.

Beef, veal or pork	−1
Bacon or sausages	−1
Hamburgers, hot dogs – fast food	−1
Fried or deep-fried food	−1
Ready meals	−1
Eggs	−1
Cheese	−1
Butter	−1
Full-fat milk or cream	−1
Pastries such as doughnuts, nut whirls etc.	−1
Sweets and chocolate	−1
Potato crisps, pretzels	−1
Ice cream	−1
Eat food every day, which is rich in roughage, like coarse wholemeal bread, fresh fruit and vegetables	+3
Don't eat food which is rich in roughage	−3
Take additional multivitamins and minerals daily	+10
(Women) Take additional calcium	+5
Keep myself informed about health and nutrition	+2

Now add up all your pluses and put them in sub-total A. Then add up all your minuses and put them in Sub-total G.

Sub-total A: +____

Sub-total G: −____

B Invariable factors
1. Sex

Male	−5
Female	+10

2. Inheritance
   Were any grandfathers or grandmothers
   over 80 years old?   +5
   What was the average age of all four
   grandparents?
   60-70   +5
   71-80   +10
   over 80   +20

3. Family history
   Did either of your parents have a stroke or
   a heart attack before the age of fifty?   −10
   −5 points for every member of the family
   (Grandparents, parents, brothers and
   sisters), who suffered from one of the
   following before their 65th birthday:
   High blood pressure   ____
   Cancer   ____
   Heart disease   ____
   Stroke   ____
   Diabetes   ____
   Another other genetically determined illness   ____

   Subtotal B: +____

                                                        −____

C Partially fixed factors
1. Family income (gross annual)
   £0-4 500   −10
   £4 500-13 500   −5
   £13 500-27 000   +1
   +1 additional point for every £9 000 up
   to £180 000   +____

2. Education
   No higher education   −7
   A levels   +2
   College   +5
   Studies or doctorate   +7

3. Career
   Academic or freelance   +5
   Self-employed   +6
   Employed in the health service   +3
   Over 65 and still in employment   +5
   Office worker   −3
   Shift worker   −5
   Unemployed   −7
   Chance of promotion   +5
   Regular contact with environmental
      pollution, toxic waste, chemicals,
      radiation   −10

4. Residential area
   City   −5
   Near an industrial estate   −7
   Rural area   +5
   Area with occasional air pollution or
      smog alarm   −5
   Area, where air pollution hinders the
      normal daily routine   −7
   Area with a high crime rate   −3
   Area with a lower or no crime rate   +3
   Residence, which has been positively
      tested for radon   −7
   Time taken to and from work
      0-½ hour   +3
      ½-1 hour   +0

-1 point deduction for every half an
hour over an hour   ____

Is there a hospital or accident hospital
within 30 miles?   +3

No hospital or accident hospital   −3

Subtotal C: +____

         −____

D Variable condition of health and check-ups

1. Present state of health

Excellent	+15
Good	+12
Satisfactory	+5
Poor	−10
Normal or low blood pressure	+5
High blood pressure	−10
Blood pressure unknown	−5
Low level of cholesterol (below 200)	+10
Medium level of cholesterol (200-240)	+5
High level of cholesterol (above 240)	−10
Level of cholesterol unknown	−5
HDL cholesterol 29 or less	−25
30-36	−20
37-40	−5
41-45	+5
above 45	+10
Unknown	−5
In a private health plan	+10
Can choose doctors	+5

2. Preventative and therapeutic measures

Women

Annual gynaecological check-up and smear	+2
Monthly self-examination of the breasts	+2
Mammography (35-50 every three years; over 50 annually)	+2
Smoking and taking contraceptive pill	−5

Men

Self-examination of the genitals every three months	+2
Rectal or prostate examination (annually over 30)	+2

Both sexes

Physiological examinations (every three to four years up to the age of 50; every one to two years over the age of 50)	+3
Recently received inoculations against mumps, measles, rubella, diphtheria, tetanus	+2
Examination for blood in the stool (over 40 every two years, over 50 annually)	+2
If over 50, annual rectal scan	+2
Active participation in a life prolongation, revitalisation or illness prevention programme	+10

3. Accident prevention

Always wear a seatbelt, as a driver or as a passenger	+7
Don't always wear a seatbelt, as a driver or as a passenger	−5
Never drink and drive or accompany a driver, who has drunk	+2

−10 points for every conviction for drink-driving in the past five years	____
−2 points for every traffic offence due to excessive speed or an accident in the past year	____
Drive over 9 000 miles annually	−1
Main vehicle weighs over 1.2 tonnes	+10
Convertible	−5
Motorbike	−10
−2 points for every fight or attack in which you were involved last year or which you witnessed	____
Fire alarm at home	+1
Subtotal D:	+____
	−____

E Variable psychological factors

Married or in a long-term relationship	+5
Satisfactory sex life	+3
Children under 18, who live at home	+3
For every five-year period of living alone	−1
No close friends	−10
+1 plus point for every close friend (up to five)	____
+2 plus points for every active membership in a religious society or relief organization (for example Red Cross) (up to four)	____
Pet at home	+2
Keep to a daily routine	+10
Hours of uninterrupted sleep per night: less than 5 hours	−5

5-8 hours	+5
8-10 hours	−7
1 minus point for every hour over 10	___
Irregular	−7
Keep to a regular working routine	+5
No regular working routine	−5
2 minus points for every five hours work exceeding 40 hours weekly	___
Take an annual holiday (at least 6 days)	+5
Regularly use a stress management technique (yoga, mediation, music etc)	+3

Subtotal E: +___

                               −___

F Variable emotional stress factors
(N = never, R = rarely, S = sometimes, A = Always or as much as possible)

	N	R	S	A
Mainly happy	−2	−1	+1	+2
Take time and like to be with my family and friends	−2	−1	+1	+2
Have my private life and my career under control	−2	−1	+1	+2
Live within my financial resources	−2	−1	+1	+2
Set myself aims and am looking for new challenges	−2	−1	+1	+2
Pursue a creative activity or hobby	−2	−1	+1	+2
Have and enjoy free time	−2	−1	+1	+2
Express my feelings easily	−2	−1	+1	+2
Like to laugh	−2	−1	+1	+2
Believe in God	−2	−1	+1	+2

Testing Times

Fly into a rage quickly	+2 +1 −1 −2
Self-critical	+2 +1 −1 −2
Critical of others	+2 +1 −1 −2
Lonely, even in company	+2 +1 −1 −2
Worry about things beyond my control	+2 +1 −1− 2
Regret having made sacrifices in life	+2 +1 −1 −2

Subtotal F: _____

Evaluation

A + B + C + D + E + F = _____ (Subtotal up to 200*)

Subtotal + G = Final total _____

*If this number exceeds 200, use 200 as the subtotal. Keep up your healthy life-style, which enabled you to achieve above-average marks and try to change some of the negative factors in section A (for example smoking) into positive values. You have a good chance of a long healthy life, as you alone can determine these factors.

Divide the final total by 2. That shows your chance (in percent) of reaching the average life expectancy of a person of your age or of having an even longer life.

Final total: _____ divided by 2

= _____ %

The Future

If you have reached one hundred percent – congratulations! But don't rest on your laurels. Keep on the look out for further possibilities of improving your health. If your marks are not as good as you hoped, remember that it is never too late to start improving your longevity potential.

Of course this test evaluation cannot be a guarantee for a long or short life, it is only to help you to analyze your way of life. A medical preparation to extend life can only have a positive effect, if it goes hand in hand with a sensible and healthy way of life. It is basically a question of preventing the decay of our cells. After all the potential for eternal youth is hidden in the cell.

CHAPTER TWELVE

All's Well That Never Ends?

Yogis who alter the function of their bodies simply through the power of the mind, anti-cancer vaccinations, superhuman immune systems, limbs that grow back, cells that don't die, artificial hearts, gene restructuring and DNA reprogramming. Where will it end? As a people our knowledge is developing exponentially. The idea is that it won't end and nor will we. The potential is at our fingertips. Not in a hundred years, not in fifty but now. There's no cure-all drug yet, no thick black tabloid headlines — yet. But, taken together these developments are the Methuselah Formula. If you give your body the respect it deserves, follow a sensible nutrition program and wait for the gene splicers to give you a helping hand you may well end up beating old Methuselah himself.

But will you want to?

That new car of yours you read about in the first chapter. Still running? Of course it is. That was the promise. You got what you paid for.

But look down your street now. Everybody else is the same. Their cars are fine too. No-one's had to trade in. Everybody's bought the wonder product. Even your neighbours down the road who vowed they'd always use public transport. A car that lasts for ever, now that's a green option. And your neighbours aren't alone. Up and down the country there's been a buying spree. Every single person in every town and village has a car, safe in the knowledge that it's the best buy they've ever made. They got what they paid for too.

What they paid for, and what you paid for, was a road system permanently gridlocked. A brilliant concept that went terribly wrong, one that overlooked a fundamental tenet of everyday life . . . we live in a world of limited resources and endless demand.

So who's to say it couldn't happen to us? If we all benefitted from a massive extension of life, wouldn't it cause society as we know it to fall apart? Our world is already over-populated as it is. The demographic changes taking place in countries with advanced welfare systems, whereby the elderly are forever increasing as a percentage of the population, are straining resources to the limit. If people stopped dying altogether, welfare provision would break down. Society would creak under the strain as more and more people entered the world and nobody left it. In the long term, it might even collapse. Who's going to feed everybody? Where are they going to live? What are they going to do?

And going back to the idea of getting what you paid for, what if you can't afford the treatment but the family on the nice side of town can? How would that make you feel? Angry? It is quite possible that such new technology would become the preserve of the rich. A new community of have-nots would be born. They'd live like we do today, while privileged others lived out their dreams, and out-lived the dreamers. And you can be sure the have-nots would want to do something about it.

Birth control of some sort would become imperative. Restrictions on how many children you could have would be a matter for law. Maybe you'd have to apply for a permit to have your own child. Maybe there would come a point where children were no longer born.

Where there are restrictions, there are usually loopholes. And if no loopholes, there's always the black market. The quacks of the middle ages would be as nothing to the con-artists profiteering from the yearnings of those who weren't allowed in on the act.

And if you did have the money, and you did have children how would you actually occupy yourself for 400 years or more? More than enough time to see every country and read every book and learn every language, but surely boredom would become a factor. The psychological effects of endless days ahead of you, and the worries of how to fill them, could be severe indeed. Euthanasia may become an option. It may even become the norm.

This is all conjecture, naturally, and it leans to the darker side of what if. Nobody knows for sure how society will change with the advent of life-extending technology, but they know it will change. Perhaps we need not fear. In the right hands, these advances could be used to alleviate suffering all over the world – no one goes sick, the agony of thousands of diseases and infections eradicated. We would find ways of meeting the strains put on the world's resources. We've always coped with change in the past, and there's no reason to think it will be any different this time.

We are at a crossroads in the development of our species. We can embrace change and move forward, or we can reject it and live and die with the consequences. I prefer the former. To halt our research (many are calling for very restrictive genetic legislation) would be to never find out what we might have become. We cannot live in fear of what the future may bring, we must shape it. History teaches us that we cannot halt evolution anyway, we can't stop our own development. Better to understand it and use it to good effect for all, than to fight it to the point that research goes on but we don't know about it, because it will, whatever the protests. We can address our fears in advance and find solutions so that when the time comes we are ready to tackle them. We must not waste this opportunity. Knowledge has become so vast, the world has become so complicated that the meagre span of human life seems insignificant in comparison. There is so much to learn, and so little time to learn it.

Let us gamble then. Let us take a chance on a course which could enable us to continually develop and improve human intellect and potential. Let us look forward to the new generation of humans who, with the advantage of almost infinite youth, will be able to responsibly determine fate with constantly increasing wisdom.

Appendix 1

Vitamin Table

Vitamin	Mainly important for	Principle sources	Deficiency symptoms
A	Vision, skin, mucous membranes and hair.	Liver, egg yolk, full cream milk, carrots, green leaved vegetables, tomatoes and apricots.	Vision disorder, night blindness, skin and mucous membrane illnesses, loss of hair, impairment of growth.
B₁	Metabolism and nerve functions.	Pulses, coarse wholemeal products, potatoes, offal, lean pork, nuts.	Disturbances of the nerve functions, stomach and intestine disorders, heart and circulation disorders, tiredness, loss of appetite.
B₂	Growth, cell respiration, metabolism, skin, mucous membranes, nail and hair.	Full-cream milk, yeast, eggs, liver, cheese, fish, green leaved vegetables, coarse wholemeal products, heart, beef, veal, chicken, tomatoes, apricots.	Skin illnesses, impairment of growth, brittle nails, photosensitivity, lips full of rents.
B₆	Proteometabolism and nervous system.	Wheat products, soya beans, potatoes, lentils, peas, offal and fish.	Skin illnesses, predominantly in the face, nervous disorders, hyperexcitability, cramps.

Appendix 1

B$_{12}$	Haemapoiesis, cellular metabolism, functioning of	Liver, kidneys, meat, milk, cheese, egg yolk, fish.	Anaemia and nervous illnesses.
Folic acid	Cell division and blood supply.	Spinach, liver, kidneys.	Anaemia, digestive disorders.
PAB (Paraaminobenzoic acid)	Growth, digestive system, skin, hair pigmentation.	Liver, beer yeast, wheatgerms, meat, nuts, fresh fruit and	Anaemia, skin rashes, tiredness, digestive disorders.
Pantothenic acid	Fat synthesis, heart and circulation.	Yeast, liver, kidneys, wheatgerms, peanuts.	Sore feet, neuritis, circulatory disorders.
B$_{15}$	Metabolism of the nervous and muscular cells, oxygen balance of the muscle and connective tissue, cerebral cortex, general functioning od the cells.	Meat, apricot seeds, rice, beer yeast, cow blood.	Metabolic illnesses and circulatory disorders, rheumatic illnesses, arteriosclerosis, illnesses of the liver.
C	Fighting-off infections, activating metabolism, gums, cellular tissue,	Citrus fruits, all types of fruit and vegetables, especially peppers,	Susceptibility to infection, tiredness, bleeding gums, delayed healing of wounds.

	formation of connective tissue and bones.	rose hips, fresh herbs.	
D	Formation of bones, regulation of the calcium and phosphorus metabolism.	Cod liver oil, spring butter, fresh milk, egg yolk, salmon, tuna.	Disorders in the mineral metabolism, rickets, dntal enamel defects, softening of the bones.
Biotin	Lipometabolism, growth, nervous system.	Yeast, liver, kidneys, egg yolk, full cream milk, peas, syrup, wheat products.	Increase in the cholesterol content in the blood plasma, delayed growth, nervous disorders, muscle pains, loss of appetite and insomnia.
Choline	Lipometabolism	Liver, wheatgerms, kidneys, brain, soya beans, asparagus, sprouts, carrots, peas, spinach, potatoes.	Digestive disorders, damage to the liver.
Inositol	Lipometabolism, skin, muscle tissue.	Heart, liver, yeast, wheatgerms, molasses, beans, peas, grapefruit, oranges,	Illnesses of the coronary blood vessels, constipation, eczema,

	Organs / Functions	Food sources	Deficiency symptoms
		peaches, apricots, strawberries, potatoes, spinach, tomatoes, egg yolk.	anomalies of the eye.
E	Gonads, lipometabolism, muscular metabolism, hormone balance.	Wheatgerms, vegetable oils, nuts.	Anaemia, weakness of heart muscles, damage to the connective tissue and to the liver, infertilitym arteriolosclerosis, lipometabolism disorders.
F	Skin, digestion, kidneys.	Cereals, wheatgerm oil, sunflower oil, soya bean oil, linseeds, olive oil.	Eczema, acne, dandruff, ulcers, diarrhoea, kidney disease, loss of hair.
K	Blood clotting.	Green plants, lucernes, spinach, cauliflower, green cabbage.	Blood clotting disorders.
P	Blood vessels.	lemon and orange peel food, rose hips, blackcurrants, grapes, buckwheat.	Capillary damage, bacterial infections, allergies. infections, allergies.

Appendix 2

My personal revitalisation programme

Healthy eating, regular physical and mental excercise are the supreme laws when it comes to maintaining or regaining your vitality or revitalising yourself. Today, however, we are able to reliably protect the body from deficiency symptoms, and so prevent premature aging, by regularly taking vital substances. Here I would like to recommend my personal programme. Don't let yourself be put off by the flood of technical terms and quantities. I am only recommending substances which are available in the stated doses as normal preparations in every chemist. You also do not have to carry a full suitcase of medicines with you to remain healthy and energetic, as many of these substances are offered as multi-preparations. Ask your chemist, and definitely ask your GP, so that any possibility of risk or incompatibility can be avoided.

I take the following daily:

1.4 mg vitamin B1 (thiamine)
4.5 mg vitamin B2 (riboflavin)
45 mg vitamin B3 (nicotinamide)
10 mg vitamin B5 (pantothenic acid)
2 mg vitamin B6 (pyridoxine)
0.005 mg vitamin B12
0.1 mg biotin
15 mg beta-carotene
500 mg vitamin C (ascorbic acid)
0.005 mg vitamin D
60 mg vitamin E
plus 1 capsule coenzyme Q10

250 mg plus magnesium – heavy magnesium oxide
  (daily 250 mg)
0.3 mg folic acid
1 dragee Helfergin 500 (centrophenoxine) after lunch
  (once a year for a period of three months daily)
200 mg pumpkin seed oil and onion oil.

In addition, I annually undergo two three-month cures
with proteolytic enzymes as well as a cure with
revitalisers (ribonucleic acids specific to the organs)
every 18 months.
  When in a state of exhaustion I have my doctor inject
me with a cocktail made up of the following ingredients:

Magnorbin (magnesium)
Cytobion (vitamin B12)
Polybion (vitamins)
Berolase (enyzmes)
Laevulose (energy supply)

Bibliography

Numerous specialist articles and books were used for *The Methuselah Formula*, which are mostly only available in the specialist libraries of scientific institutes and to which the non-scientist has little or no access. Therefore only some of the important popular publications are listed here.

Barrows, C.H./Beauchene, R.E. – Aging and Nutrition. Published in Albanese, A.A.: Newer methods of Nutritional Biochemistry (Vol. 4, Academic Press, INC. New York 1970).

Beier, W. – Biophysikalische Aspekte des Alterns multizellulärer Systeme (VEB Georg Thieme, Leipzig, Volume 16, 1973).

Bek, Lilla/Pullar, Philippa – Chakra-Energie, Bern 1987.

Blumenthal, H.T. – The Regulatory Role of the Nervous System in Aging (Basel, S. Karger, 1970).

Böhlau, V. – Wege zur Erforschung des Alterns (Scientific Book Society, Darmstadt 1973).

Boyd, Doug – Swami Rama, Munich 1983.

Budge, E.W.W. – The Life and Exploits of Alexander the Great, London 1896; The History of Alexander the Great, London 1889.

Buttlar, Johannes v. – Die biologische Chance, Munich 1981; Der Menschheitstraum, Düsseldorf 1975; Drachenwege, Munich 1990; Die Wächter von Eden, Munich 1993.

Cadmore, Larison – Der Stoff des Lebens, Frankfurt/M. 1978.

Carrington, Patricia – Das große Buch der Meditation, Bern 1992.

Carnac, Pierre – Geschichte beginnt in Bimini, Olten 1978.

Carson, C – The Roquish World of Doctor Brinkley

Bibliography

(Holt, Rhinehart and Winston, New York, 1960).

(Sri) Chinmoy – Kundalini, Zürich 1992; Die Kraft der Mantren, Zürich 1992.

Cooper-Oakley, Isabel – Comte de St. Germain, London 1912.

Comfort, A – The Process of Aging, New York, Signet Science Library, 1961 (Signet Book P2452); Basic Research in Gerontology (Gerontologia, 16: 48-64, 1970); Die biologischen Grundlagen des Alterns (Theodor Steinkopff Publishers, Dresden 1969); Aging: The Biology of Senescence, New York, Holt, Rhinehart and Winston 1956 (Library Congress Card 64-15946).

Dalley, Stephanie (Publ.) – Myths from Mesopotamis, Oxford 1991.

Dennis, E./Harman, D. – Free Radical Theory of Aging: Effect of Adding Antioxidants to the Maternal Diet on Life Span of Offspring (Omaha, Nebraska 68105, 1974).

Dixon, Patrick – The Genetic Revolution, Lottbridge Drive 1993.

Ettinger, R.C.W. – The Prospect of Immortality (New York, Doubleday and Co. NIC., 1964).

Feuerabendt, Sigmund, und Hammer, Dr. med. Oscar – Yoga und die Ärzte, Luxembourg 1982.

Franke, H. – Hundertjährige (Publishing house of the Franconian Society Press) Würzburg 1971; Aktuelle Probleme der Gerontologie und Geriatrie (Naturwissenschaften 61, Springer Publishers 1974).

Frolkis, V.V. – Aging of a Cell (Gerontology and Geriatrics, 1970-1971 Year Book).

Fulcanelli – Master Alchemist (Neville Spearman, London 1971).

Bibliography

Fuller, Jean Overton – The Comte de Saint Germain, London 1988.
Gaitz, Ch.M. – Aging and the Brain (Plenum Press, New York/London 1972).
Gilgamesch Epos – Philipp Reclam Jun., Stuttgart.
Harman, D. – Free radical theory of aging dietary implications (The American Journal of Clinical Nutrition 25, August 1972); Increasing the Healthy Life Span (Omaha, Nebraska); Free Radical Theory of Aging (Triangle, Vol. 12, No. 4, 1973); Prolongation of Life: Role of Free Radical Reactions in Aging (Official Journal of the American Geriatrics Society, August 1969); Free Radical Theory of Aging: Effect of the Amount and Degree of Unsaturation of Dietary Fat on Mortality Rate (Journal of Gerontology 1971, Vol. 26, No. 4, 451-457); Free Radical Theory of Aging: Effect of Vitamin E on Tumor Incidence (Meeting of the Gerontologists 1967); The Free Radical Theory of Aging: Effect of Age on Serum Copper Levels (Journal of Gerontology 1965); The Biologic Clock: The Mitrochondria? (Omaha, Nebraska 68105, April 1972).
Hauer, J.W. – Der Yoga, Südergellersen 1983.
Hinze, Oscar Marcel – Tranta Vidya, Freiburg 1983.
Keeton, Kathy – Longevity, New York 1992.
Klossowski de Rola, St. – Alchemie (Droemer, Knaur, München/Zürich 1974).
Longevity Potential Test – Longevity New York 9/90.
McCall, Henrietta – Sumerian Myths, London 1990.
Mookerjee, Ajit/Khanna, Madhu – Die Welt des Tantra, Bern 1987.
Orzechowski, G. – Das Phänomen des Alterns in historischer und molekular-biologischer Sicht, Hypothesen und Folgerungen (Physikalische Medizin

und Rehabilitation, Januar 1974, Heft 1).

Pakesch, E. – Die Behandlung und Prophylaxe arteriosklerotischer Geistesstörungen (Wiener klinische Eochenschrift, Springer Publishers, Vienna–New York, Nr. 12, P. 211-215, 1970).

Patanjali – Die Wurzeln des Yoga, Bern 1979.

Pauling, L. – The Process of Aging (Reprinted from New Dynamics of Preventative Medicine, edited by Leon R. Pomeroy. Published by Symposia Specialists, Miami, Florida 1974); Good Nutrition for the Good Life (Engineering and Science, June 1974); Vitamin C and the Common Cold (Pan/Ballantine, London 1972).

Popper, K.R., und Eccles, J.C. – Das Ich und mein Gehirn, Munich 1982.

(Swami) Rama – Living with the Himalayan Masters, Honesdale 1978.

Rosenfeld, Albert – ProLongevity, New York 1976.

Scientic American Special Issue – Life, Death and the Immune System, New York, September 1993.

Sitchin, Zecharia – Stufen zum Kosmos, Unterägeri 1982.

Unschuld, P.U. – Pen-Ts'ao. 2000 Jahre Traditionelle Pharmazeutische Literatur Chinas (Heinz Moos Publishers, Munich 1973).

(Swami) Vivekananda – Raja Yoga, Freiburg 1983.

Wolf, M./Ransberger, K. Enzyme Therapy (Vantage Press, New York 1972).

Eolf, N. – Möglichkeiten und Erfolge der Zelltherapie bei hirnatrophischen Prozessen (Fortschritte der Medizin 1969).

Woodhouse, H.W. – Aspects of the Biology of Aging (Symposia of the Society for Experimental Biology, No. 21, New York Academic Press 1967).